Literature & Thought

WHAT'S SO FUNNY?

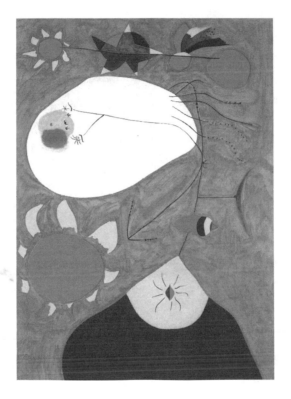

Perfection Learning

EDITORIAL DIRECTOR	Julie A. Schumacher
SENIOR EDITOR	Terry Ofner
EDITOR	Rebecca Christian
PERMISSIONS	Laura Pieper
REVIEWERS	Claudia Katz
	Sue Ann Kuby
	Larry Bargenquast
	Mary Gershon

DESIGN AND PHOTO RESEARCH   William Seabright and Associates,
Wilmette, Illinois

COVER ART PORTRAIT IV 1938 Joan Miró

ACKNOWLEDGMENTS

"The Adoption of Albert" from *My Brother Louis Measures Worms* by Barbara Robinson. Copyright © 1988 by Barbara Robinson. Used by permission of HarperCollins Publishers.

Excerpts from *Anguished English* by Richard Lederer (Wyrick & Company). Copyright © 1987 by Richard Lederer. Reprinted by permission of Wyrick & Company.

"Beware the Ides of November" from *I Love You, I Hate You, Get Lost* by Ellen Conford, published by Scholastic, Inc. Copyright © 1994 by Conford Enterprises, Ltd. Reprinted by permission of McIntosh & Otis, Inc.

"The Clown" from *Real Ponies Don't Go Oink* by Patrick F. McManus. Copyright © 1991 by Patrick F. McManus. Reprinted by permission of Henry Holt and Company, LLC.

"A Conversation With My Dogs," from *What The Dogs Have Taught Me* by Merrill Markoe. Copyright © 1992 by Merrill Markoe. Used by permission of Viking Penguin, a division of Penguin Putnam, Inc.

"Fish Eyes" from *Nobody Ever Sees You Eat Tunafish* by David Brenner. Copyright © 1986 by David Brenner. Reprinted by permission of the William Morris Agency, Inc. on behalf of the author.   CONTINUED ON PAGE 144

Why Do We Need Humor?

The question above is the *essential question* that you will consider as you read this book. The literature, activities, and organization of the book will lead you to think critically about this question and to develop a deeper understanding of humor.

To help you shape your answer to the broad essential question, you will read and respond to four sections, or clusters. Each cluster addresses a specific question and thinking skill.

CLUSTER ONE What makes *you* laugh? **EVALUATE**

CLUSTER TWO How is humor used? **ANALYZE**

CLUSTER THREE What are some types of humor? **CLASSIFY**

CLUSTER FOUR Thinking on your own **SYNTHESIZE**

Notice that the final cluster asks you to think independently about your answer to the essential question—*Why Do We Need Humor?*

FUNNY

Sometimes laughter erupts

from deep volcanic soul space

surprising solemn moments like

blue crocuses in spring snow

Nagueyalti Warren

TABLE OF CONTENTS

"You Have to Be There"

Ways of Making Yourself Laugh

Laugh aloud right now.

Go ahead!

Everyone loves to laugh, including you. Besides, medical science has established that laughter offers numerous health benefits. It is also a great help in coping with countless difficult situations. So get started! The topic of this book is humor, so why aren't you laughing already? Treat yourself to a good, hearty belly laugh.

Perhaps you find this difficult to do. "I haven't read anything funny yet," you might be saying, "so how can I laugh?" This need not stop you. It *is* possible to laugh even when there is nothing funny to laugh about.

Take a lesson from actors, who must laugh uproariously when the script demands it. (This is much more difficult than crying on cue.) First, pant rhythmically like a dog. Then add an "ah" to your panting. With some practice, you will soon be able to laugh as loudly and as long as you want.

The above technique just might be the world's only sure-fire, foolproof technique for producing laughter. Jokes and humorous stories are unreliable. How often has someone told you a joke that left you cold—or even offended or embarrassed? ("You had to be there," is the familiar excuse for a misfired joke.) When it comes to humor, one person's meat is another's poison. The joke that can make *everybody* laugh, anytime, anywhere, is yet to be invented.

So this anthology does not come with a guarantee that you will laugh at every humorous selection in it. With a little luck, at least one piece will bring a giggle, a chuckle, or even an out-and-out fit of guffaws. Other pieces won't even bring a smile.

Can a comedy sketch dating to the first half of the twentieth century still tickle the funny bone? For some readers, yes.

And of course, this anthology also includes informational selections which aren't meant to be funny. Writers—especially humorists—sometimes turn oddly serious when trying to explain the nature of laughter.

But you can learn something even from selections in this book that don't make you laugh. There is at least one human being who has laughed at every humorous piece included here, and the more serious pieces may help you understand why this is so.

This is good. Finding out what amuses other people is one of the most important things you can learn about the human species. For indeed, laughter is one of the defining traits of a human being. The ancient Greek philosopher Aristotle declared that of all living creatures, only humans laugh. Countless thinkers since his time have echoed the sentiment.

So to be a more *human* being, the thing to do is laugh. If you want to laugh right now, you know how to do it. Just pant like a dog and vocalize until the laughter starts. But you're not likely to enjoy it very much. You'll probably feel as if you missed the point of a joke. To really enjoy a gale of laughter, you simply "have to be there."

Take a chance on this anthology. Your quest for something funny may seem hit-and-miss from time to time. But sooner or later, real laughter will hit, and you'll have a great time.

Comedy: A Serious Business

Praticing goofy faces in the mirror, telling a joke over and over until the timing is perfect, scanning the headlines for new material, rehearsing painful pratfalls, such is the work of comedy. As in music, painting or any other art, the hardest part is making it look easy.

"Nothing's quite so wonderful as those waves of love and applause splashing over the footlights - and nothing quite as shattering as when an audience doesn't like you."

Lucille Ball

"The secret source of humor itself is not joy but sorrow."

Mark Twain

"All of my pictures are built around the idea of getting into trouble and so giving me the chance to be desperately serious in my attempt to appear as a normal little gentleman."

Charlie Chaplin

"Those two fellows we created, they were nice, very nice people. They never get anywhere because they are both so dumb, but they don't know they're dumb. One of the reasons why people like us, I guess, is because they feel superior to us."

Stan Laurel

"I'm not the best jokesmith in the world, but what I've tried to bring is a sense of style and a sense of someone who can say things in a funny and serious and touching way. I've tried to show that you don't have to yell to be heard."

Billy Crystal

"I've heard stories that the stand-up comic is like the most courageous, most dangerous. I don't know. It depends. So if you bomb, you bomb. Once you get used to bombing, had the experience, you just have it. All you have to do is just share that you're bombing."

Lily Tomlin

"I never forget a face, but in your case I'll make an exception."

Groucho Marx

"I hope that comedy remains open and fun and loose and free, and that people remember tolerance . . ."

Whoopi Goldberg

CONCEPT VOCABULARY

You will find the following terms and definitions useful as you read and discuss the selections in this book.

black humor humor that comes from situations that are grim or tragic

burlesque old-fashioned humorous theatrical entertainment made up of exaggeration, comic skits, and sometimes striptease

business a movement, action, or saying that is part of a comic routine

comedienne a female comic

comedy humorous entertainment

court jester a person who provides amusement for a king or queen and the ruler's court

cynicism the attitude that people and the world are generally bad (which can be a source of humor)

farce a light drama with broad comedy and a hard-to-believe plot

flat characters overly simple characters of whom only one side is shown

formula a tried and true method to get laughs

gag writer a person who writes jokes, skits, or funny situations, usually for a comic, television, or the movies

gallows humor humor in the face of pain or death

humor something that is funny because it is surprising or absurd; something thought to be comical or amusing

improvisational comedy a spontaneous instead of a scripted comedy routine

irony what happens when the real outcome is different than the expected outcome (for example, when a rich woman wins the lottery)

joke something said or done to provoke humor, generally a short spoken story with a funny twist at the end

lampoon to mock or make fun of

parody a literary or musical work in which the style of an author or composer is closely mimicked for comic effect (for example, many of the songs of Weird Al Yankovic)

practical joke a joke that relies on something being done rather than something being told

prank a trick that is meant to amuse

pratfall a fall taken on purpose to be funny

pun a play on words (for example, "That's not punny!")

punch line the climax of a joke

rounded characters characters that seem real because more than one side of them is shown

sarcasm a sharp, often funny comment, meant to mock and/or give pain

satire a story or play in which sarcasm or wit are used to expose and ridicule people's mistakes, vanities, and bad habits

scatological humor humor that relies on bathroom functions to get laughs

shtick a routine, gimmick, or gag for which a comic is known (for example, Rodney Dangerfield's signature line, "I don't get no respect.")

sit-com a comedy, usually on television, in which humor grows out of an incident or situation

slapstick broad humor (like that of the Three Stooges) that relies on physical actions such as falling down

stand-up comedy a humorous monologue delivered by a comic who is usually standing up on a stage

tall tale a story that relies on exaggeration for comic effect

vaudeville an old-fashioned form of light theatrical entertainment that generally uses some combination of pantomime, dance, song, dialogue, and acrobatics

wisecrack a clever or sarcastic remark

wit the skill of being able to think quickly and often humorously, and/or a person who uses this skill

CLUSTER ONE

What Makes You Laugh?

Thinking Skill EVALUATING

HEE HEE
HEE HEE

HA HA
HA HA

Memories of Dating

Dave Barry

As a mature adult, I feel an obligation to help the younger generation, just as the mother fish guards her unhatched eggs, keeping her lonely vigil day after day, never leaving her post, not even to go to the bathroom, until her tiny babies emerge and she is able, at last, to eat them. "She may be your mom, but she's still a fish" is a wisdom nugget that I would pass along to any fish eggs reading this column.

But today I want to talk about dating. This subject was raised in a letter to me from a young person named Eric Knott, who writes:

"I have got a big problem. There's this girl in my English class who is really good-looking. However, I don't think she knows I exist. I want to ask her out, but I'm afraid she will say no, and I will be the freak of the week. What should I do?"

Eric, you have sent your question to the right mature adult, because as a young person, I spent a lot of time thinking about this very problem. Starting in about eighth grade, my time was divided as follows:

Academic Pursuits: 2 percent

Zits: 16 percent

Trying to Figure Out How to Ask Girls Out: 82 percent

The most sensible way to ask a girl out is to walk directly up to her on foot and say, "So you want to go out or what?" I never did this. I knew, as Eric Knott knows, that there was always the possibility that the girl would say no, thereby leaving me with no viable option but to leave Harold C. Crittenden Junior High School forever and go into the woods and become a bark-eating hermit whose only companions would be the gentle and understanding woodland creatures.

"Hey, Zitface!" the woodland creatures would shriek in their cute little Chip 'n' Dale voices while raining acorns down upon my head. "You wanna *date*? Hahahahahaha."

So the first rule of dating is, Never risk direct contact with the girl in question. Your role model should be the nuclear submarine, gliding silently beneath the ocean surface, tracking an enemy target that does not even begin to suspect that the submarine would like to date it. I spent the vast majority of 1960 keeping a girl named Judy under surveillance, maintaining a minimum distance of fifty lockers to avoid the danger that I might somehow get into a conversation with her, which could have led to disaster.

Judy: Hi.

Me: Hi.

Judy: Just in case you have ever thought about having a date with me, the answer is no.

Woodland Creatures: Hahahahahaha.

The only problem with the nuclear-submarine technique is that it's difficult to get a date with a girl who has never, technically, been asked. This is why you need Phil Grant. Phil was a friend of mine who had the ability to talk to girls. It was a mysterious superhuman power he had, comparable to X-ray vision. So, after several thousand hours of intense discussion and planning with me, Phil approached a girl he knew named Nancy, who approached a girl named Sandy, who was a direct personal friend of Judy's and who passed the word back to Phil via Nancy that Judy would be willing to go on a date with me. This procedure protected me from direct humiliation.

Thus it was that, finally, Judy and I went on an actual date, to see a movie in White Plains, New York. If I were to sum up the romantic ambience[1] of this date in four words, those words would be, "My mother was driving." This made for an extremely quiet drive, because my mother, realizing that her presence was hideously embarrassing, had to pretend she wasn't there. If it had been legal, I think she would have

---

1 **ambience:** atmosphere

got out and sprinted alongside the car, steering through the window. Judy and I, sitting in the back seat about seventy-five feet apart, were also silent, unable to communicate without the assistance of Phil, Nancy, and Sandy.

After what seemed like several years, we got to the movie theater, where my mother went off to sit in the Parents and Lepers Section. The movie was called *North to Alaska,* but I can tell you nothing else about it because I spent the whole time wondering whether it would be necessary to amputate my right arm, which was not getting any blood flow as a result of being perched for two hours like a petrified snake on the back of Judy's seat exactly one molecule away from physical contact.

So it was definitely a fun first date, featuring all the relaxed spontaneity of a real-estate closing,[2] and in later years I did regain some feeling in my arm. My point, Eric Knott, is that the key to successful dating is self-confidence. I bet that good-looking girl in your English class would *love* to go out with you. But *you* have to make the first move. So just do it! Pick up that phone! Call Phil Grant. ∾

2 **real-estate closing:** a meeting to finalize the sale of property

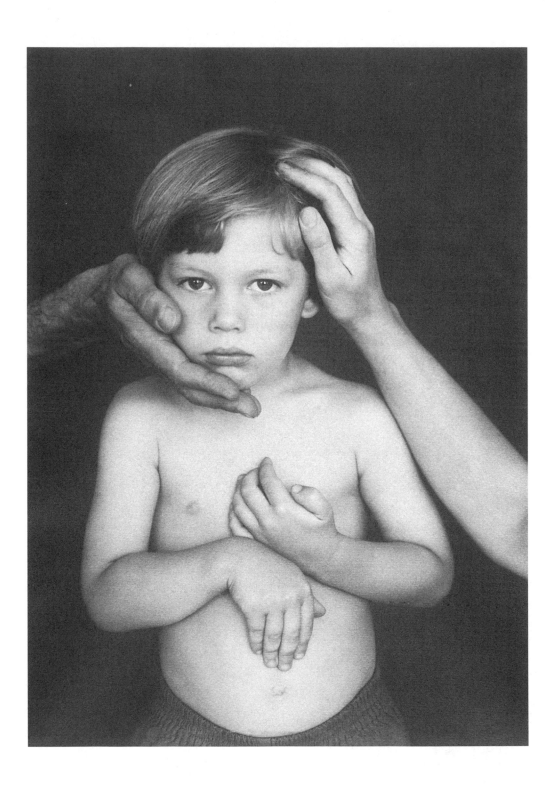

The Adoption of Albert

BARBARA ROBINSON

There were so many children in our neighborhood that my mother was never surprised to find unfamiliar ones in the house, or in the backyard, or in my room, or in Louis's room.

"Well, who's this?" she would say, and she would then go on to connect that child with whatever house or family he belonged to.

But when Louis showed up with his new friend Albert, Mother had other things on her mind: the family reunion, which was two days away; the distant cousin who would be staying at our house; most of all, my Aunt Rhoda's famous Family Reunion cake, which, in Aunt Rhoda's absence, Mother felt obliged to provide.

Aunt Rhoda's absence, and the reason for it, were both first-time events: She had never before missed a family reunion, and neither she nor anyone else had ever before been called into court to testify about anything. Aunt Rhoda was to testify about an automobile accident she had witnessed—the only automobile accident in local memory, my father said, that did not involve Aunt Mildred.

All in all, it was a complicated time for Mother—cake, cousins, company—and when Louis appeared at the kitchen door and said, "This is Albert," she was too distracted to ask her usual questions.

Nor did she ask them at suppertime. By then she was up to her elbows in cake batter and left the three of us to eat alone with my father, who also didn't know Albert, but assumed that everyone else did.

I didn't know Albert either, but there was no reason why I should. He was Louis's friend, he was Louis's age, he even looked a lot like Louis—small and quiet and solemn—and it didn't occur to me to find out any more about him. I did ask, "Where do you live, Albert?"; and when he said, "Here," I just thought he meant here in the neighborhood instead of someplace else.

Mother thought the same thing. "Where does that little boy live?" she asked me the next morning, and I said, "Here," and she said, "I wonder which house?"

Albert had spent the night, and there was a note propped against the cereal box: *Albert and I have gone to dig worms.*

Louis had been collecting worms all summer and measuring them to see how long a worm got to be before it died. "I think that's what kills them," he said. "I think they die of length."

So far his longest worm was between four inches and four and a half inches. All his worms were between one size and another because they wouldn't hold still. "It's really hard," he said. "I have to stretch them out and measure them at the same time, and if I'm not careful they come apart."

"Oh, Louis," I said, "that's awful! What do you do then?"

He shrugged. "I bury the pieces. What else can I do?"

Of course, most kids wouldn't even do that, but Louis was neater than most kids.

It was late afternoon when he and Albert came back, and they had big news. They also had two coffee cans full of worm parts.

"I thought you buried them," I said.

"I didn't have to! Albert says . . . Albert says . . ." I had never seen Louis so pleased and excited. "Tell her what you said."

"It doesn't kill them," Albert said. "The tail ends grow new heads, and the head ends grow new tails."

I looked in the coffee cans, but I couldn't tell the difference between head and tails. Louis said he couldn't tell the difference either. "But it doesn't matter," he said, "because the worms can. *They* know. We're going to keep them, and watch them grow, and measure them . . . and maybe name them."

"They're no trouble," Albert said. "They just eat dirt. We've got some." He held up another coffee can.

They took all three coffee cans up to Louis's room, and this worried me a lot because I knew I would have to sleep in Louis's room when everybody came for the family reunion.

My father said he was always astonished that there was anybody left to *come* to the family reunion. "Your whole family is already here," he told Mother, "living around the corner, or three streets away, or on the other side of town."

"Not everybody," Mother said. "There's Virginia and Evelyn and Clyde . . ." She reeled off the names—cousins, mostly, whom we knew only from Christmas cards, and from their annual appearance at the reunion.

Some, in fact, had already appeared and were upstairs unpacking their suitcases. Mother, who was busy catching up on their news and shuffling food around in the refrigerator and getting out all the dishes and silverware, either didn't realize that Albert was still with us or just didn't remember that she had ever seen him in the first place.

My father had gone off to borrow picnic tables for the next day, and since I didn't want to sit around and watch worms grow, I went next door to play with my friend Maxine Slocum and forgot all about Albert.

That night when I took my sleeping bag into Louis's room, he was already asleep in a mound of bedclothes . . . and there was another mound of bedclothes beside him.

"Louis." I shook him awake. "Who is that?"

"It's Albert," he said.

"Why doesn't he go home?"

Louis looked surprised. "He *is* home. He's going to live here now. Remember? He told you. . . . Don't worry, Mary Elizabeth," he added. "You'll like Albert."

"I already like Albert," I said, "but I don't think he can live here. I think he has to live with his parents."

"He doesn't want to," Louis said. "He even told them so. He told them, 'I don't want to live with you anymore,' and they said, 'All right, Albert, you just go and live someplace else.'"

I had never heard of such a thing, except when my friend Wanda McCall baptized the hamsters with her mother's French perfume. The house smelled wonderful, but all the hamsters got sick and so did Mrs. McCall, and Mr. McCall gave Wanda two dollars and told her to get lost. But he didn't mean forever.

Neither had Albert's parents, I decided. They would probably call tomorrow and tell him to come home.

"Louis." I shook him again. "Where are the worms?"

"They aren't worms yet," he reminded me. "The cans are in the closet."

I didn't think either half of a worm could go very far, but I put my sleeping bag on the other side of the room anyway, just in case.

When I woke up the next morning Louis and Albert were gone, but they had made the bed and folded up their clothes and left a note that said, *We'll be back for the picnic. Please don't move the worms.* There was a P.S.: *Tell the lady cousin in the purple underwear that I'm sorry. I didn't know she was in there.* Then there was another P.S.: *It was really Albert, but pretend it was me and tell her I'm sorry. Or if you don't want to, just find out who she is and I'll tell her.*

That was nice of Louis, I thought, but I really didn't want to ask around about everyone's underwear.

"I guess not," Louis said later. "It's okay . . . Albert felt bad about it, that's all."

"Where is Albert?" I asked.

"Over there." Louis pointed to where Mother's brother Frank was taking pictures with his new Polaroid camera.

"You'll have to get closer together," we heard him say, "and put Clyde's boy in front of you, Blanche."

"Who is Clyde's boy?" Louis asked me.

"I think it's Albert," I said. "He's the only boy there."

I was right. "Looks just *like* Clyde," we heard Aunt Blanche say.

I thought Albert looked a little worried, but Louis said he was just worried about the worms. "We're going to move them someplace else," he said. "Albert thinks they might get out and crawl around—especially the head parts, Albert said, because they could see where they were going."

That made me shiver, so I hoped they would put them somewhere up high.

By then Aunt Rhoda had arrived, to everyone's surprise. She never did get to testify, she said, because "the litigants"[1] had to go to the police station to look at "mug shots" and "supply ID's." Aunt Rhoda had picked up a whole new vocabulary.

"Mug shots?" my father said. "ID's? Now, what does that mean? This was a traffic accident, not a holdup."

"I don't know," Mother told him. "Rhoda just said they had to study mug shots of children."

"There is no such thing as mug shots of children. Mug shots are of criminals. Rhoda's got it all wrong." He went to question Aunt Rhoda further and stumbled into the one event he always tried to avoid: the big family photograph, with everyone in it.

---

1 **litigants:** people involved in a lawsuit

Uncle Frank had set up a different camera and lined everybody up, but he was missing some people: my parents, Aunt Mildred . . . "And Louis," he said. "And Clyde's boy. Clyde, where's your boy?"

Clyde looked surprised. "He's in the Army."

"I mean the little one."

"Looks just like you," Aunt Blanche put in.

"He doesn't look one bit like me," Clyde said. "He looks like his mother."

"No," Aunt Blanche said stubbornly. "He looks like you."

Clyde was stubborn too. "How do you know what he looks like, Blanche? You haven't seen him in six years!"

"I saw him fifteen minutes ago!"

"Who?" my father said, arriving on the scene with Mother.

"They're talking about Albert," I said. "Louis's friend Albert."

"Albert!" Mother looked amazed. "Is that little boy here again?"

"He never left," I said.

So I was sent to get Albert, and find out where he lived, while Mother explained to everybody who he was (which was hard, because she didn't *know* who he was), and my father pressed Aunt Rhoda for more details about her experiences in court—fearful, he later said, that she had wandered into the wrong courtroom and the wrong trial, and was now mixed up with a bunch of criminals.

I found Louis crawling around the floor of his room. "We dropped some of a worm," he said, "but only one, and I'll find it. We took the rest of them out of the closet."

"Mother wants to know where Albert lives," I told him.

"You mean . . . besides here?" Louis was being stubborn too, just like Aunt Blanche and Clyde. "I don't know."

"Well, what's Albert's name?"

"You mean . . . besides Albert? I'll ask him."

"But, Louis—don't you know?"

"I only met him day before yesterday," Louis said. "He was sitting on the curb outside the model-airplane store, after his parents told him to go live someplace else. He didn't know anyplace else, so I told him he could live here. And after that, all we talked about was worms."

Albert didn't know where he lived either. "I can't remember," he said. "We haven't lived there long enough for me to remember. I think it's the name of a tree."

Albert was right. He lived on Catalpa Street, and his name was Henderson. But it was Aunt Rhoda, of all people, who supplied the information, while Louis and Albert were upstairs looking for the missing worm.

Aunt Rhoda recognized Albert in the Polaroid picture because, when she witnessed the automobile accident, she had also witnessed Albert in one of the cars with his parents—the very same people, she said, who were at this moment examining mug shots at the police station.

"Isn't it a small world!" Aunt Rhoda said . . . and everyone agreed, except my father.

He had assumed, all along, that Mother knew who Albert was and knew where Albert came from. "And I suppose," he said, "that Albert is staying with us now because his parents have to be in court—but didn't the Hendersons mention *why* they had to be in court?"

"I don't know the Hendersons," Mother said.

"Well, did Albert . . ."

"I don't know Albert either." Mother was getting testy under all this cross-examination. "Obviously, Louis said it would be all right for Albert to stay here—and it *is* all right," she said. "Those poor people have enough trouble. That's the least we can do for them."

In the meantime Louis and Albert came downstairs—"We found the worm," Louis assured me—went to get more fried chicken and potato salad, and ran into Aunt Rhoda, who said she was certainly surprised to see Albert again and to see him *here.*

"I live here," Albert said.

"Oh, no," Aunt Rhoda laughed. "You live on Catalpa Street."

"Not anymore," Albert said.

Of course Aunt Rhoda reported this to Mother, who was by then completely mystified about Albert, and pretty fed up with all the sketchy bits and pieces of news about him. She left Aunt Rhoda to cut the Family Reunion cake and make the coffee, and went off to find Louis. My father, having also concluded that Louis was the key to it all, had done the same thing.

Between them, they quickly figured out that Louis did not know the Hendersons and that he barely knew Albert . . . and that Albert had left home and was prepared to live with us forever.

My father called the police station, where the Hendersons were indeed studying pictures of missing children and supplying information about their own missing child . . . and in no time they arrived at our house and were reunited with Albert.

This was exactly the kind of happy ending my mother loved best—even Albert seemed happy to be back with his family.

"Well, now he has a friend," Mrs. Henderson said, beaming at Louis. "That was the trouble. He didn't know anyone, didn't have anyone to play with or talk to. Thank goodness for you, Louis!"

The Hendersons obviously saw Louis as the hero of it all, which exasperated my father.

"I don't know why you're so grumpy," Mother said. "Just suppose Louis hadn't come along and found Albert outside the airplane store—then what?"

"Then Albert would have gone home where he belonged," my father said, "and none of this would have happened."

"Exactly!" Mother said. "And he would still be a lonely, unhappy little boy . . . way over there on Catalpa Street."

She invited the Hendersons to stay for cake and coffee, and to meet all the relatives. Aunt Rhoda said she couldn't meet them officially, or talk to them, because of being a witness, but she waved to them from the back porch, and Mrs. Henderson waved back and called to her, "Your cake recipe is wonderful!"

"Have some coffee," Mother said. "It's Rhoda's coffee, too."

Aunt Rhoda said later that it was pretty silly to call it *her* coffee just because she'd made it, and she also said that she didn't feel one bit responsible for what had happened.

"In my house," she said, "if a can says coffee, that's what's in it, and it wouldn't occur to me to look."

Mother said, in all fairness, it wouldn't occur to her to look either. . . . "Except, of course, I don't keep my coffee on that high shelf, so I might have looked."

My father, who had been the first one to sip the coffee—and, therefore, the *only* one to sip the coffee—said he wished *someone* had looked.

"Was it the can full of dirt?" I asked Louis, and he shook his head no.

"Oh, I'm sorry, Louis," I said, "but you and Albert can get some more worms."

"And it was only the tail ends, anyway," Albert said . . . although I hadn't really wanted to know that. ଔ

Say Good Night, Gracie

George Burns and Gracie Allen

Editor's note: George Burns and Gracie Allen were a beloved comedy team—married to each other in real life—whose joint career spanned the eras of vaudeville, radio, and television. George was the "straight man" to Gracie's scatterbrained character who got all the laughs. Burns didn't mind. Years after her death, he said, "No, I'm not nervous before going on stage. When I worked with Gracie, Gracie got nervous. To get nervous, you gotta have a lot of talent, and Gracie had the talent."

(As this scene begins, music plays, and George and Gracie enter holding hands. Gracie stops, turns, looks toward the wings, and waves. She lets go of George's hand and walks toward the wing, still waving. Then she stops and beckons to whomever she is waving to come out. A man comes out, puts his arms around Gracie, and kisses her, and she kisses him. They wave to each other as he backs offstage. Gracie returns to George center stage.)

GRACIE. Who was that?

GEORGE. You don't know?

GRACIE. No, my mother told me never to talk to strangers.

GEORGE. That makes sense.

GRACIE. This always happens to me. On my way in, a man stopped me at the stage door and said, "Hiya, cutie, how about a bite tonight after the show?"

GEORGE. And you said?

GRACIE. I said, "I'll be busy after the show but I'm not doing anything now," so I bit him.

GEORGE. Gracie, let me ask you something. Did the nurse ever happen to drop you on your head when you were a baby?

GRACIE. Oh, no, we couldn't afford a nurse, my mother had to do it.

GEORGE. You had a smart mother.

GRACIE. Smartness runs in my family. When I went to school I was so smart my teacher was in my class for five years.

GEORGE. Gracie, what school did you go to?

GRACIE. I'm not allowed to tell.

GEORGE. Why not?

GRACIE. The school pays me $25 a month not to tell.

GEORGE. Is there anybody in the family as smart as you?

GRACIE. My sister Hazel is even smarter. If it wasn't for her, our canary would never have hatched that ostrich egg.

GEORGE. A canary hatched an ostrich egg?

GRACIE. Yeah . . . but the canary was too small to cover that big egg.

GEORGE. So?

GRACIE. So . . . Hazel sat on the egg and held the canary in her lap.

GEORGE. Hazel must be the smartest in your family.

GRACIE. Oh, no. My brother Willy was no dummy either.

GEORGE. Willy?

GRACIE. Yeah, the one who slept on the floor.

GEORGE. Why would he sleep on the floor?

GRACIE. He had high blood pressure—

GEORGE. And he was trying to keep it down?

GRACIE. Yeah.

GEORGE. I'd like to meet Willy.

GRACIE. You can't miss him. He always wears a high collar to cover the appendicitis scar on his neck.

GEORGE. Gracie, your appendix is down around your waist.

GRACIE. I know, but Willy was so ticklish they had to operate up there.

GEORGE. What's Willy doing now?

GRACIE. He just lost his job.

GEORGE. Lost his job?

GRACIE. Yeah, he's a window washer.

GEORGE. And?

GRACIE. And . . . he was outside on the twentieth story washing a window and when he got through he stepped back to admire his work.

GEORGE. And he lost his job.

GRACIE. Yeah . . . . And when he hit the pavement he was terribly embarrassed.

GEORGE. Embarrassed?

GRACIE. Yeah . . . his collar flew off and his appendicitis scar showed.

GEORGE. Gracie, this family of yours—

GRACIE. When Willy was a little baby my father took him riding in his carriage, and two hours later my father came back with a different baby and a different carriage.

GEORGE. Well, what did your mother say?

GRACIE. My mother didn't say anything because it was a better carriage.

GEORGE. A better carriage?

GRACIE. Yeah. . . . And the little baby my father brought home was a little French baby so my mother took up French.

GEORGE. Why?

GRACIE. So she would be able to understand the baby—

GEORGE. When the baby started to talk?

GRACIE. Yeah.

GEORGE. Gracie, this family of yours, do you all live together?

GRACIE. Oh, sure. My father, my brother, my uncle, my cousin and my nephew all sleep in one bed and—

GEORGE. In one bed? I'm surprised your grandfather doesn't sleep with them.

GRACIE. Oh, he did, but he died, so they made him get up.

GEORGE. Say good night, Gracie.

GRACIE. Good night, Gracie. ∾

Beware the Ides of November

ELLEN CONFORD

A red-letter day! All the signs are in your favor! Take advantage of the many wonderful opportunities that come your way!"

That's what my horoscope said for Thursday, November 12th.

And it wasn't one of those one-size-fits-all horoscopes that run in the daily newspapers. This was a personalized astrological forecast prepared *"Especially for you, NIKKI FELDMAN!"* by famed astrologer and psychic Stella Amarillo.

"She's uncanny," my friend Bess had raved. "Almost everything she predicted for me came true. Just try it for a month. It only costs nine ninety-five."

Well, it was November, and the weather was bleak and raw and rainy, and I was going through one of those dismal periods when my spirit felt as dreary as the weather.

Anything, I thought, to break the tedium. So I sent Stella Amarillo $9.95 (plus postage and handling) and received my Monthly Forecast and Predictions on November 9th.

I was pretty impressed for the first two days. For the 10th my horoscope said, "Be careful of what you wish for today. It might come true."

I spent the whole morning wishing I didn't have to take the biology test seventh period, because I had spent all of last evening reading the stuff Stella Amarillo had sent.

And right after lunch I had to race out of English to the girls' room, where I spent fifteen minutes throwing up. The nurse said there was a virus going around, but I was sure it was the cafeteria's meat loaf.

Whatever it was, I spent the rest of the afternoon on a cot in the health office, and didn't have to take the biology test.

So I got what I wished for, but it wasn't pleasant.

Then on Wednesday my forecast said, "Financial concerns are foremost in your mind today." As it turned out, I'd forgotten my wallet and didn't have any lunch money. (Which may have saved me from another case of food poisoning, come to think of it.)

Not exactly earth-shattering predictions, but close enough for Bess to say, "See? I told you she was incredible!"

Then came November 12th, my "red-letter day," the day of wonderful opportunities, the day all the signs were supposed to be in my favor.

From the time I left the house that morning, every sign I ran into read: DANGER, SLIPPERY WHEN WET! BEWARE OF DOG! DON'T EVEN THINK OF PARKING HERE!!

The first wonderful opportunity came my way on the school bus. There was an empty seat. Unfortunately, it was next to Duane Bellinger. I hesitated because Duane Bellinger is a very unappealing person, who for some mysterious reason, seems to like me.

"Hey, Feldman, move it!" Robby Randazzo pushed me forward. I remembered Stella Amarillo's advice. Take advantage of every opportunity. Sitting down was better than standing up, right?

Wrong.

Robby shoved me into the seat. I landed—heavily—on Duane's lunch bag. I felt the squoosh and jumped up. Duane grabbed the bag, Robby Randazzo laughed uproariously, and I felt something damp and slimy on the seat of my jeans.

"What *is* that?" I screeched. I jumped up and craned my neck around, trying to see my rear end.

"My jelly sandwich," Duane said apologetically. "Open-faced. I'm trying to drop a few pounds."

"Aw, no!" I moaned. "Is that grape? It's all over my pants!"

Duane handed me a napkin. Robby offered to help me wipe off the jelly.

I dabbed futilely at my jeans. "What kind of a diet are you on?" I growled at Duane. "You put a quart of jelly on a piece of bread and you leave the top off to save calories?"

He looked miserable. I didn't know which bothered him more—that he'd ruined my jeans or that I'd ruined his lunch.

I headed for the girls' room the minute I got into school. I washed out as much of the grape jelly as I could in the sink, and held my pants up to the hand blower to dry.

It took forever. And when the jeans were dry, instead of a wet, gooey purple stain, I was left with a dry, stiff purple stain. And was ten minutes late to math class. So that everyone could see me walk to my seat in the last row with a purple splotch on my backside.

But in gym class, things began to look up. We were playing basketball, and I was still so angry at Duane and Robby Randazzo that I channeled all my hostility into the game.

I scored three baskets, two foul shots, and stole the ball twice. Ms. Carlton was very impressed.

"Fantastic, Nikki! You really played above yourself today."

"It's a good way to blow off steam," I panted.

"That's what I keep trying to tell you girls," she agreed. "If you can play like that consistently, you ought to try out for the team."

"I don't think so," I said. "I haven't usually got this much steam to blow off."

I don't always shower after gym, but this time I needed to. I washed up quickly and towel-dried my hair. I had a history test next period, which I would have enough trouble with even if I started on time.

Shelby Gutierrez lent me her dryer so I could do a fast blow out, just enough to look semidecent. I plugged it into a socket next to the mirror, flicked it on, and all the lights in the bathroom went out.

"Nikki! What did you do to my dryer?" Shelby pulled it away from me. "You broke it."

"She didn't break your dryer," someone else said. "She shorted out the locker room. Everything's dark."

"What makes you think it's my fault?" I asked irritably. "Maybe there's an outage in the whole building."

There was. But it didn't last long. Just long enough so that all I could do with my wet hair was to drag a comb through it and let it hang.

Just long enough for me to have to dress in near darkness, so that I didn't see that I had closed my locker door on the loose end of one thread—*one thread*—of my yellow Shaker-knit[1] sweater.

---

1 **Shaker-knit:** a style of knitting in which the yarn is closely interlaced

Just long enough to be out of the locker room and halfway up the stairs before Bess said, "Nikki, do you know your sweater's coming apart in the back?"

"What are you talking—"

I felt her finger run down my bare spine. "It's completely separated," she said.

"What? How could—"

The lights flickered on again.

"Look at that," she said. "You've got a thread loose. It's stretched all the way back to—"

"No," I moaned. "Oh, please, *no.*" I twisted around. Sure enough, a strand of cotton trailed behind me. My sweater was divided halfway up my back, exposing quite a few inches of skin, and the clasp of my bra.

I slumped against the banister. "What am I going to do?" I wailed.

"Well," Bess began, "if you want to save the sweater, you'd better follow the thread back to the locker room."

"I mean now! For the rest of the day! I can't go around like *this.*"

"Do you have an extra shirt or anything down here?" she asked.

"Only my gym shirt."

"I guess you'd better wear it."

"I can't wear that! It's all sweaty."

"All right, calm down," she said. "I'll go upstairs to your locker and get your jacket. Do you think it's long enough to cover that stain on your jeans?"

"If it was long enough to cover the stain on my jeans," I shrieked, "I wouldn't *have* a stain on my jeans! I'd have a stain on my jacket!"

She bolted up the stairs as if she wanted to get away from me as fast as possible.

And who wouldn't? I was a walking disaster zone. If one more "wonderful opportunity" came my way, I'd wrap that loose thread around my neck and hang myself.

I sighed pitifully and twisted the cotton strand around my finger. I wanted to break off the thread before the whole sweater unraveled. But the cotton was too strong. No matter how hard I tried, I couldn't break it.

There was only one thing to do. I started back toward the locker room, following the trail of the thread, gathering it up as I walked, like Theseus in the labyrinth.[2]

2 **Theseus in the labyrinth:** in Greek mythology, Theseus used a thread to guide himself out of a labyrinth, or maze, in which he was trapped

I must look awfully stupid, I thought. The one piece of luck I'd had so far today was that there was no one in the hall to see me.

I'd just reached the door to the gym when I heard footsteps on the stairs. Boy, that was fast, I thought. Bess must have run all the way.

"Thank goodness you're back," I said. "Two seconds more and I'd have been half-naked."

But it wasn't Bess.

"Then I'm sorry I didn't wait two seconds."

It was Steve Landis. Nice, smart, very attractive Steve Landis. For whom I'd harbored a secret longing for almost three months. Whom, at any other time, I would have been overjoyed to run into in an empty hallway.

I shrank back against the wall, clutched my books to my chest, and tried not to cry. But my misery must have shown on my face.

"Is something wrong, Nikki?" He came toward me. "You look like you're trying to hide from someone."

"No, no." My voice was shrill and unnatural. "Everything's fine."

Everything's just dandy. I finally get to be alone with Steve Landis, and my hair is wet and my sweater is coming apart and I have grape jelly on my jeans and I sound hysterical.

"Take advantage of the many wonderful opportunities that come your way!"

How? I can't move from this spot, he's thinking of me half-naked, and my voice has all the appeal of a chain saw.

At which moment Bess came running down the stairs yelling, "Nikki, I can't get your locker door open," and someone shoved the door of the gym out. It smashed into my back, sending me sprawling facedown on the floor.

"Nikki!" Three voices blended into one cry, and I groaned in pain.

I turned my head to the side. My eyes felt as if they were spinning in their sockets. Three sets of knees appeared in my line of vision. I was pretty dazed. I wasn't sure if there were really three people squatting next to me, or one person with six legs.

"I think I'm seeing triple," I whispered.

"Oh, Nikki, I'm sorry." Ms. Carlton's voice. "I didn't realize . . ."

Three pairs of hands reached down to help me to my feet. (Or one person with six arms, if I was seeing triple.)

"You poor kid," Steve said as I tried to steady myself on my feet. "Do you think anything's broken?"

"Only my faith in Stella Armarillo."

"Oh, dear," said Ms. Carlton. "She might have a concussion. We'd better get her to the nurse."

"Lean on me," Steve said. "I'll help you." He and Bess each put an arm around my waist and steered me toward the stairs.

My head clanged like a gong and my knees buckled as I walked.

"My thread," I told Bess. "I have to get the rest of my thread."

"Geez," said Steve sympathetically, "she must be delirious. And look at her sweater. It's completely wrecked."

▲   ▲   ▲

"You're having a rough week," said the nurse as I lay on the same cot where I had recovered from meat loaf poisoning two days before.

I had an ice pad behind my head, an ice pack on my forehead, and was holding two ice cubes wrapped in a washcloth against my nose.

A scratchy wool blanket covered the rest of me, up to my chin. It felt itchy, even over my clothes, but all that ice was making me so cold that my teeth chattered. Which made my head hurt.

Every fifteen minutes the nurse peered into my eyes with a little flashlight, looking for signs of concussion.

And to make things absolutely perfect, Duane Bellinger lay on the cot next to me, separated only by a thin curtain, sneezing, coughing, and complaining that he had malaria.

In between sneezes, coughs, and moans, he begged my forgiveness for the jelly sandwich incident, and for my hand in marriage, if we both recovered.

When the nurse checked my eyes for the third time, I was feeling a little better. I pulled off the ice packs and began to worry about being in such close contact with Duane.

"Is malaria catching?" I asked her.

"He hasn't got malaria." She smiled. "Just allergies."

"The way my luck is running, I'll catch his allergies."

"Can I come in?" Steve Landis poked his head through the office door. "How's she doing?"

"I think she's going to be fine," the nurse said. "I want to get her X-rayed, but I can't reach her folks at work. I'll keep trying."

He moved close to my cot and looked down at me. At my swollen nose, my tangled hair, the egg-shaped lump on my forehead, which by now was probably an unbecoming shade of blue.

"Gee, you look awful."

"I know."

"Is there anything I can do for you?"

Just stop looking at me, I wanted to say. Just go away and come back when the bruises fade and my hair is brushed, and I'm wearing clothes that don't look like I stole them from a bag lady.

"Steve? Steve Landis, is that you?" Duane called from behind the curtain.

"Duane?" Steve pushed the curtain aside. "What's the matter? Your allergies again?"

"I think it's malaria. Did Nikki tell you we're engaged?"

"We're not engaged, Duane!" I sat up and swung my legs over the edge of the cot. "I'm getting out of here." I felt the air on my back as my sweater parted down the middle.

Would this day ever be over? Was there no end to the humiliation that I had to endure?

"There is something you can do for me," I told Steve. "If you could get my jacket from my locker, I'd really apprec—"

A sharp series of bells interrupted me.

"Fire drill," Steve said.

The nurse shook her head. "There's no fire drill scheduled for today."

"Attention please!" The principal's voice boomed over the PA system. "This is not a drill. It is imperative that we evacuate the building immediately. Your teachers will lead you in a calm and orderly manner to the nearest exit. I repeat, this is *not* a drill."

"Okay, kids, let's go," the nurse said.

"I can't go out like this," I said. "Let me get my jacket."

"It's probably just a bomb threat," Steve said.

"That's right," I agreed. "We have them a couple of times every year and there's never any bomb. Please don't make me go out like this."

Duane leaped to his feet and grabbed my arm. "I'll save you, Nikki." He yanked me up from my cot and sneezed on me.

"Take the blanket with you and let's go," the nurse ordered. "Duane, get moving."

"I'll help her." Steve draped the blanket over my shoulders. I clutched the edges together under my chin. He put his arm around me and guided me out of the office, into the stream of students surging down the hall.

Here was the moment I'd dreamed of for three months. Steve Landis, with his arm around me.

And bomb threat or no bomb threat, people noticed us.

"Hey, look!" yelled Robby Randazzo. "Sitting Bull."

"It can't be Sitting Bull," someone else said. "She's standing. Maybe it's Mother Teresa."

"No, Gandhi!" Shelby said as she passed us. "Nikki looks like Gandhi."

I lowered my head and fixed my eyes on the floor as Steve led me, in a calm and orderly manner, out of the building.

As we massed in the schoolyard, with my classmates more concerned with my hideous appearance than the possibility of the school blowing up, I answered the question I'd asked myself before.

No. This day would never be over. And no. There was no end to the humiliation I would have to endure.

▲   ▲   ▲

But the day did end.

And the school didn't blow up. The nurse was able to reach my father, and the X rays were negative. I didn't even have a concussion.

That night I reread my horoscope.

"Thursday, November 12. A red-letter day! All the signs are in your favor! Take advantage of the many wonderful opportunities that come your way!"

Snarling like a dog, I crumpled my horoscope into a ball and hurled it across the room. It landed in my tropical fish tank.

"Nikki, honey, are you all right?" my mother called. "Do you need anything?"

"Not unless you know a good exorcist!"[3]

I started toward the aquarium to check my fish for injuries when the phone rang.

"Hey, Nikki, it's Steve. How's your head?"

"Steve?" I sat down on the edge of my bed and clutched the phone to my ear. "Steve Landis?"

"Why are you so surprised?"

"Well—I didn't expect you to call." *Ever.*

"I feel sort of responsible for what happened," he said. "If I hadn't surprised you like that—"

"It's not your fault," I said. "It's my sweater's fault."

3 **exorcist:** one who gets rid of an evil spirit or demon

"How did the X rays turn out?"

"Fine," I said. I told myself he was just being nice because he felt guilty. I told myself he was just being nice because he was a basically nice guy. I told myself that anyone who'd seen what I'd been through today would be concerned.

There's no reason, I warned myself, to read more into Steve's call than simple courtesy.

I would be courteous, too. "I should have called to thank you," I said. "You went to a lot of trouble for me today."

"It wasn't any trouble," he said. "Do things like this happen to you a lot?"

I couldn't help laughing. "Only on my good days."

I explained to him about the horoscope, and then went on to describe everything that had gone wrong, up to the time Ms. Carlton slammed the gym door into me.

By the time I finished we were both laughing, and I realized we'd been on the phone for almost half an hour. This is more than simple courtesy, I thought. He could have hung up after I told him I was fine.

"Well," he said, "maybe you got all your bad luck a day early. And nothing will happen to you tomorrow."

"Tomorrow? Why should anything happen to me tomorrow?"

"Nikki, you're following your horoscope and you don't know what day tomorrow is?"

"It's Friday," I said, still puzzled. And then it hit me.

"Friday the thirteenth!" We both shouted it into the phone at the same time. We both groaned at the same time.

"It can't be any worse than today," I said when we finished groaning.

"Maybe I'd better keep an eye on you tomorrow, just in case," he said.

"Keep an eye on me?" When I had my hair brushed and decent clothes on and wasn't seeing triple?

"Can I pick you up in the morning?" he went on. "I'm a very careful driver. Never had an accident."

I heard a thumping sound. "That's me, knocking on wood," he explained.

I was speechless. Steve Landis wanted to keep an eye on me. Steve Landis wanted to drive me to school. I could hardly breathe, let alone answer him.

"Nikki? Are you still there?"

I gulped. "Yes. Could you hold on a minute, please?"

I walked slowly to the fish tank and pulled the soggy horoscope from it. I squeezed out as much water as I could and carefully uncrumpled it.

I could just make out the forecast. "Friday, November 13: You may find this Friday the 13th living up to its reputation. Unlike yesterday, aspects are rather unfavorable. Postpone signing contracts or making long-term financial commitments. Above all, avoid joint partnership ventures."

I smiled happily and went back to the phone.

"Nikki, what are you doing?"

"Just checking my horoscope," I said.

"What did it say?" he asked.

"It said I should absolutely not let you drive me to school tomorrow."

He laughed. "It didn't really say that, did it?"

"Absolutely," I giggled.

For a moment he was silent. Then he said, "Okay. So should I pick you up around 7:45?"

I smiled into the phone even though he couldn't see me.

"Absolutely," I said. ‿

Letters from a Nut

TED L. NANCY

Letters from a Nut, *in which the following letters appear, is a collection of goofy correspondence between comedian Ted L. Nancy and the unsuspecting businesses and organizations to which he sends off-the-wall requests. Nancy writes establishments such as the Ritz Hotel asking if he can appear in the lobby in a bladder costume or begging for toenail clippings swept from the floor of a celebrity guest room. Nancy's world is a wacky one. Comedian Jerry Seinfeld, who claims to have "discovered" Nancy and who has written the introductions for Nancy's books, says, "From his Las Vegas shrimp costume to . . . his lost bag of otter hair, it's hard to figure out what's driving this guy."*

Nancy writes the letters "straight," and the polite, if perplexed, responses to them are real ones that came back from corporate spokespersons who may not have realized that they were being spoofed.

Seinfeld adds in his introduction, " . . . I knew from the beginning that I had to do everything I could to let as many people as possible read the hilarious truth about what has been going on inside the mailbox of Ted L. Nancy, whoever he may be."

Here's Seinfeld's advice on how to read the letters: " . . . if you should find yourself in possession of this book, one of the great joys of it is definitely reading the letters out loud."

560 No. Moorpark Rd. #236
Thousand Oaks, CA 91360

Oct 25, 1996

Administration
THE COCA COLA COMPANY
1 Coca Cola Plz., NW
Atlanta, GA 30313

Dear Coca Cola:

I have a beverage called Kiet Doke. Will it interfere with your beverage—Diet Coke. The taste is NOT SIMILAR at all!! (Mine tastes like Pepsi).

I sell my Kiet Doke to mostly construction workers who love it. One guy said, "This sure DOESN'T taste like Coca Cola."

Let me know so I can continue to sell my soda. Thanks. By the way do you use caramel in your soda? Just checking. Thanks.

Sincerely,

Ted L. Nancy

Ted L. Nancy

The Coca-Cola Company

COCA-COLA PLAZA
ATLANTA, GEORGIA

LEGAL DIVISION

January 9, 1997

ADDRESS REPLY TO
P.O. DRAWER 1934
ATLANTA, GA 30301

404 676-2121
OUR REFERENCE NO.

Mr. Ted L. Nancy
560 No. Moorpark Road #236
Thousand Oaks, CA 91360

RE: KIET DOKE (Our Reference Number 145342)

Dear Mr. Nancy:

Thank you for your letter of October 25, 1996 inquiring whether you may continue using the trademark KIET DOKE in association with a beverage.

As the owner of a federal registration for the famous trademark "diet Coke", we cannot consent to your use of KIET DOKE in association with a beverage. We believe KIET DOKE is confusingly similar to our trademark "diet Coke", and are concerned that an appreciable number of consumers will believe that The Coca-Cola Company endorses your product. As a result, we must insist that you immediately take action to discontinue use of KIET DOKE.

If you are willing to immediately cease and desist using KIET DOKE, and agree not to use any product name or trademark similar to trademarks of the Coca-Cola Company in association with beverages in the future, please sign the spaces provided and return this letter to me. If you would like to discuss this, I may be reached at the numbers below. If we have not received this signed agreement within fifteen (15) days of the date of this letter, we will assume you do not agree to these terms.

Sincerely,

Nancy V. Stephens
Trademark Counsel
(404) 676-3035-Telephone-(404) 676-7682-Fax

Acknowledged and agreed to
this_____day of _____, 1997
on behalf of _____

_____ _____

SIGNATURE OF OFFICER

_____

560 No Moorpark Rd. #236
Thousand Oaks, CA 91360

Mar 29, 1997

MS. NANCY V. STEPHENS
COCA COLA
PO Drawer 1734
Atlanta, GA 30301

Dear Ms. Nancy V. Stephens,

I have decided that I will <u>not</u> sell my KIET DOKE beverage any more. The product is discontinued. I am taking my $700.00 out of the bank and my 11 cans of Kiet Doke that are left and bringing them home. (They are in my room now).

I now realize it was a poorly thought out idea. It was stupid. I mean if you went to 7-11 and saw in the cooler Dr. Pepper, Orange Crush, Wink, and Kiet Doke would you choose Kiet Doke? I don't think so. The idea was bad. Who was I to think that someone would choose Kiet Doke? I am embarrassed over what I now consider to be a terrible idea.

So let this letter stand as my admission that I have ceased and desisted. There will be no more Kiet Doke on the market. I am sorry I bothered you. I am sorry I wasted your time.

And please look out for my new beverage—PIET DEPSI. With the familiar slogan: "It Tastes Nothing Like Coke!" (Will be in coolers soon). Piet Depsi is a thirst quenching drink which, I believe, does not taste like your drink.

Enjoy it! Also, what about the caramel in your soda? Are you using a lot of it? Thanks.

Respectfully,

Ted L. Nancy

Ted L. Nancy

560 No. Moorpark Rd. #236
Thousand Oaks, CA 91360

Mar 31, 1997

MAYOR'S OFFICE, JACKSON
145 Broadway St.
Jackson, OH 45640-1656

Dear Mayor's Office,

I want to give back to the community. I want to stage the
play "Romeo and Juliet" using otter. There will be no racy
scenes but some holding. Otters will play Romeo, Juliet, and
the others. We will bring the otters out at intermission to
pet. These otters are something to see. They have performed
this play many times with only one biting incident.

I wish to put on a FREE performance in your downtown area
for workers. Or any other people the Mayor's Office deems
necessary. I want to give back to the community. Perhaps you
have some folks that could use a good otter rendition of this
classic love story. This is a sensitive, warm telling of the
story using sea otters. Audiences will like the otter grunts
and sounds especially when Romeo tells Juliet he loves her.

Ohio is the place. I have grand memories of the towns of
this great state.

Please let me know how I put on this free show for the good
people of Jackson? Thank you. Would you like to see a video
tape of the show? I look forward to hearing from you soon.
All I require are three stair ramps and a public address
system.

Sincerely,

Ted L. Nancy

Honorable
John T. Evans
Mayor
(614) 286-3224

Memorial Building
145 Broadway
Jackson, Ohio
45640

City of Jackson
Office of the Mayor

April 15, 1997

Mr. Ted L. Nancy
560 No. Moorpark Rd. #236
Thousand Oaks, CA 91360

Dear Mr. Nancy:

Thank you for your letter of March 31,1997, informing us that you would like to stage "Romeo and Juliet", in our area, using otter.

This sounds quite interesting; before we schedule a free show, we feel that we "otter" (no pun intended) view a video-tape of the show. Could you please send this to me; then, after reviewing the tape, I will contact you.

Again, thank you for your interest in our City; I look forward to receiving the video-tape.

Sincerely,

John T. Evans
Mayor
City of Jackson, Ohio

JTF/rrp

RESPONDING TO CLUSTER ONE

WHAT MAKES YOU LAUGH?

Thinking Skill EVALUATING

1. Dave Barry often uses exaggeration, or **hyperbole**, to create humor. To see how this writer works, find two examples of exaggeration in "Memories of Dating." Then explain the aspects of dating that Barry is exaggerating.

2. A sit-com, short for "situation comedy," is a television show in which humor arises out of situations that are funny because they are surprising, chaotic, or confusing. If you were a television producer, which of the stories in this cluster would you choose as the starting point for a television series? Explain your answer.

3. Some people think Ted Nancy's "Letters from a Nut" are hilarious, harmless fun. Others think they are irresponsible because they waste the time of people who must respond to him. **Evaluate** these points of view; then tell with which you agree and why.

4. Different things are funny to different people. Use the Laugh-O-Meter chart below to **evaluate** the humor quotient of each selection in the cluster on a scale of one to five, with one being the least funny and five being the funniest. As your teacher directs, compile the data and determine the class favorite.

Title	Laugh-O-Meter Ranking (1-5)	Reason for Ranking
Memories of Dating		
The Adoption of Albert		
Say Good Night, Gracie		
Beware the Ides of November		
Letters from a Nut		

Writing Activity: Evaluating What Makes You Laugh

Write an essay explaining which you think is the most or least funny selection in this cluster. Your evaluation should list three reasons why your choice is or isn't funny. Illustrate each reason with an example from the selection.

A Strong Opinion Essay

- begins by stating your opinion
- lists clear reasons for your opinion
- gives examples that support your reasons
- summarizes your opinion

CLUSTER TWO

How Is Humor Used?
Thinking Skill ANALYZING

HEE HEE
HEE HEE

HA HA
HA HA

Fish Eyes

DAVID BRENNER

Ladies and Gentlemen and Children of all ages (drum roll, please), I am proud to bring to you, from its very beginning to its very ending, the very true and hopefully very funny story of little David Brenner and his fish eyes.

Let's have a brief background of the Louis and Estelle Brenner offspring. The oldest, Mel, "Moby Dick"; the middle, Blanche, "Bib"; and the itsy-bitsy little baby, David, "Kingy." Very close and very much in love with one another in spite of great differences in age and lifestyle. Whatever sibling rivalry existed was expressed lovingly in the wildest, weirdest, most bizarre practical jokes and most disturbingly creative attacks. The oldest was the most devious. For example:

My brother offered me a delicious new drink—and I discovered—pure carrot juice. He pretended to join me in drinking some. I didn't pretend, taking the biggest gulp of all time of the most rancid-tasting liquid of all time, almost causing me to throw up on the spot. The oldest rolled on the floor bursting with laughter as I charged upstairs to brush my teeth and gargle. The youngest strikes back. Every night I poured just a few drops of the awful carrot juice into my brother's milk. Every night he complained that his milk tasted rather peculiar but continued to drink it until all the juice was consumed. As the last glass was finished, I announced what I had been doing. His turn to brush and gargle.

The oldest also had the sickest sense of humor. His idea of fun was to sneak up on me while I was reading or sleeping and place a dirty sock of his on my shoulder or over my face. Now remember that this is a man tormenting a boy, a full-grown man with a Ph.D. degree, a college professor, a brilliant intellect. I'd be watching TV and all of a sudden I'm smothered with a dirty gym sock, or I'd be doing my homework and suddenly would smell something rotten, only to see the sock my brother was dangling in front of my forehead. I was never safe in my own house, not even when I went to sleep in the bedroom I shared with my big, demented brother. When he would return home after a date, he would sneak up to the bed and lay a dirty sock over my sleeping face. Sometimes he would pile as many as a half-dozen socks on my face. Of course, I struck back as best I could. For these sock wars, we wouldn't put our dirty socks in the clothing hamper to be washed. My mother was always complaining about the missing socks. So as not to aggravate Mother and in order to better aggravate each other, we both began wearing the same socks for a week or so while throwing clean socks into the hamper. My mother was happy, and we developed more deadly sock bombs.

My best attack ended the war forever. While my brother was out on a date, I rigged a series of clothesline pulleys across the ceiling of my bedroom, through which I put a string, on the end of which was a rancid sock. When lowered, this foul article of clothing would come to rest directly above my brother's pillow. A second dreadful sock was rigged so that it could be pulled across his pillow. I then tied the string to my hand and forced myself to stay awake until my brother returned from his date.

In the middle of the night he came home. I faked deep breathing as I heard him climb into our bed. I waited until I heard the familiar sound of his sleeping breathing, then I ever so slowly pulled the string that released the sock so that it hung a few inches above his nose. As he sniffed, twisted and turned onto his side, I pulled the string that brought the other sock slowly sliding up onto and across his pillow, coming to rest directly at his nose. He sniffed, coughed, and opened his watering eyes, and stared at the moldy cloth object perched at the tip of his nose. I then released the pulley string so that the first sock came pummeling from the ceiling. A direct hit—right over his face. My brother gagged and shot up. I rolled around the bed in hysterics. Moby Dick, on the merits of originality and ingenuity, conceded victory and called a truce. So ended the War of the Socks.

Warfare with sister Bib was of an entirely different nature. She had a proof-perfect aim. She could hit just about any target, from any distance, with just about any weapon, her favorite being a rubber band with a semistraightened paper clip or a V-shaped wad made from tightly rolled paper. Then, too, she could throw anything, from a sofa pillow to a stale end of a rye bread, with the same deadly skill. I would tease her, she'd pick up something, I'd run as quickly as I could, she'd haul off and throw, I'd get smacked with it. I never learned my lesson. What I should have done was tease her from behind a protective shield or from another city.

Now for the fish-eye incident. One day I challenged a friend of mine to a game of stickball.[1] . . .

The fellow I challenged to a game was the best, or second best, according to me, stickball player in the neighborhood. We were to play longways on my street. Kids from all over the neighborhood came to see the playoff.

We flipped a coin and he won. I would bat first. I got myself positioned at home plate, a small pothole in the street. The first pitch was a big mistake on his part. It was low and on the outside, just where I liked it. I knew it was going to be a home run as soon as the bat left my shoulder, and it would've been, if I hadn't gotten hit in the back of the head with a small red brick.

I collapsed to the street. I didn't know what or who had hit me. I saw who as soon as I rolled over onto my back. There she was, my sister, running across the roofs.

The game was called off. I got to my feet dizzily and staggered toward my house. A huge lump was already coming out on the back of my head. It looked like a person was following me. When I got into the house, I didn't say anything to my mother, because there was an unwritten rule in the streets that one never squeals. It was a sacred law.

I weaved into the kitchen, where my mother was preparing fish for dinner. The lump on my head reflected a large shadow on the wall.

Now, preparing fish for dinner was different in those days. Nowadays you go to a supermarket and there's a fish counter and inside are all the fish already prepared for you. You reach in, you take a white thing wrapped in cellophane paper marked "Fish." It could be anything—a gym sock, anything. When I was a kid, it was a lot different, especially if you were poor. Your mother either went to the local fish market or bought the fish off a pushcart. No matter where you bought it, you had to prepare the fish yourself. It wasn't cleaned. You bought the whole fish, with the head and the tail, a little hat, eyeglasses, sneakers, the works.

---

1 **stickball:** baseball adapted for play in the streets with a broom and a lightweight ball

Then the fisherman would wrap it up in a newspaper. I still feel a little squeamish when I open a newspaper, because as a kid, sometimes you'd open a paper and under the headlines there'd be this open-mouthed carp staring at you.

Next, your mother had to prepare the fish herself. She had to cut off the head and the tail and put in her own mercury.[2] It was entirely different then and it was difficult.

While my mother was preparing the fish for dinner, I was standing there wobbling, thinking of how I could get revenge on my sister. I glanced down on the drainboard of the sink and saw a pair of fish eyes staring at me. I scooped them up and put them in my pocket. I got some Krazy Glue and glued them to my forehead and then climbed into the dirty clothing hamper in the hallway with a flashlight in my mouth, the light flashing inward. I waited until my sister opened the hamper to throw in some of her delicacies, then I turned on the flashlight. When my sister saw my red cheeks and the four eyes, she fainted, but, as she fell, she slammed the lid of the hamper against the end of my flashlight, lodging it in my throat. Immediately, I climbed out of the hamper and started running down the hall. My mother saw me, thought I had jammed a pipe in my throat and my eyes were coming out of my head. She collapsed on the spot. I charged downstairs. My father glanced up. Nothing ever bothered my father. He just looked at me and said, "How ya doin', four-eyes?"

My father followed me into the kitchen, where I was removing the fish eyes from my forehead, after having successfully extracted the flashlight from my throat. Lou took a long puff on his cigar and slowly blew the smoke up to the kitchen ceiling. He removed the cigar from his mouth and looked at me. Then in his soft, Godfather-type whisper, he spoke: "Kingy, I want you to take those fish eyes into the backyard and throw them into the garbage can or else I'm going to see that you eat them for dinner."

I didn't need more convincing. I ran out into the backyard, opened the garbage can lid and . . . well, I looked into the eyes of the eyes. It was as if we had become friends. I just couldn't throw my new-found friends into the garbage just like that. They were pleading with me to save them, silently promising that they could offer me more fun. I opened the lid and rattled the can noisily, as though I were throwing away the eyes,

2 **mercury;** a poisonous metallic element; due to water pollution, traces of it sometimes appear in fish bought in grocery stores today

which was really dumb because there was no way two eyes could make that much noise. You could throw away an entire cow more quietly.

I then carefully put the fish eyes into my pocket and went into the house. I apologized to my sister and mother for the incident. Then I casually walked into the dining room and as silently as possible slid open the top drawer of the dresser where the glue was kept. I took the glue and ducked out into the back alley. I then reglued the fish eyes to my forehead and walked up to 60th Street, the bustling shopping area for the neighborhood.

I would walk up to a store whose front window was painted halfway up in order to use the space for advertising, and then I would tap on the window lightly but loudly enough to be heard while simultaneously raising my head so that the fish eyes would appear first and then my own wide-open eyes. Women shoppers would scream. I did it to about six stores. The rumor was flying that a monster was loose on 60th Street. The neighborhood was terrorized. I was very happy.

I returned to my house and placed the two fish eyes in the center drawer of my bedroom dresser, a hand-me-down from my brother, who had as a child put a big ball of roofing tar in the center drawer. I think he was trying to corner the black-tar market.

Well, you know the attention span and memory span of young children. It isn't very long. The world is all new and all exciting, and there is so much to enjoy and remember that one forgets so much, such as a pair of fish eyes casually placed in a drawer.

The summer rolled along. July came and with it a horrific heat spell. The second floor of our house began to stink. Then the first floor. The whole house reeked of a strange and horrible odor. Although we really could not afford to call an exterminator, we were forced to, because we would gag upon entering the house, and my father's search for the dead animal had failed. We had no choice—Morris the Exterminator Man.

He arrived in his exterminator truck, which had a huge water bug on the roof almost as big as the truck itself. The water bug was on its back with its legs up in the air, and Morris's slogan was painted across the side paneling: "Nobody Gets Away Alive from Morris the Bug Killer."

Morris came into the house and sniffed around. He went up the stairs to the second floor. I could hear him open the door to my bedroom and enter. I think I even remember hearing him sniffing around in there. I know I do remember hearing him scream and seeing him charge down the stairs.

"What is it, Morris? Have you found it?"

"Yes, it's a dead animal."

"What kind of animal?"

"I don't really know, Mrs. Brenner. I've never seen anything like it in my life. It's in the center drawer of David's dresser. It's this real small, soft, black animal and from the look of its eyes, I'd say it's been dead at least two years."

My father, mother, sister, and brother snapped their heads in my direction. I leaped to my feet and ran out of the house. There was no way I was going to have fish eyes and tar for dinner.

That's the truth, the whole truth, nothing but the truth about the pair of fish eyes as it all happened during one of those glorious summers so long ago in the days of my wild, woolly, disturbed—and fun-filled—youth. Would I do it all over again if I could? You're darn right I would. ∾

Life's a Sketch

MICHAEL NEILL

BOB CALANDRA

Sunny is adorable, loves Dr. Seuss and is going through the terrible twos. Tess is adorable, a Dr. Seuss fan—and also a victim of the terrible twos. Tess's father is Robb Armstrong, who draws *JumpStart,* the syndicated cartoon in which Sunny appears.

Armstrong and his wife, Sherry, insist that they—and Tess—have their own lives, separate from those of Joe, Marcy and Sunny, the loving, hard-working family in *JumpStart*. Still, the lines do blur. Armstrong admits to having modeled Marcy and Sunny on his wife and daughter, and "when things happen to me, they go right into the strip," he says. Adds Sherry: "Sometimes after my mom reads Robb's strip she'll call and say, 'Did that really happen?'"

Whatever the cartoon's source, the daily lives of Joe, a policeman, Marcy, a nurse, and Sunny—along with a supporting cast of family and friends—have helped make Armstrong one of the country's hottest young newspaper cartoonists. His strip, which runs seven days a week, is syndicated in 350 papers, and HarperPerennial has published *JumpStart: A Love Story,* a novel in cartoons. "He does wonderful work," says Charles Schulz, creator of *Peanuts.* "A strip needs good characters—and that's what *JumpStart* has."

Armstrong also thinks *JumpStart,* most of whose characters are black, tells an important story. "It flies in the face of racial stereotypes," he says. "Joe and Marcy are such normal, everyday people, committed to doing the jobs they are paid to do."

They weren't always so mainstream. When Armstrong first launched the strip, his characters spoke in street slang. "I was trying to be blacker," says Armstrong. "Then a black woman wrote me, and she was just irate. I said, 'You know, she's right—I don't use this slang.' I was feeding into all those stereotypes."

In fact, Armstrong has always had good luck listening to the women in his life. Growing up in the working class Wynnefield section of Philadelphia, the youngest of five children, the cartoonist-to-be never knew his father, who abandoned the family soon after Robb's birth. His older brother Billy served as a substitute until he was killed in a subway accident at 13, when Robb was 6. But it was his mother, Dorothy, a seamstress, who always encouraged Robb to develop his talent, enrolling him in private art classes when he was 10. She also got him into Shipley, a prestigious Main Line private school—then refused to accept a full scholarship. "She insisted on paying half even though she didn't have it," Armstrong says. "She was accustomed to providing for our family."

Dorothy Armstrong saw her son graduate from Shipley and go on to Syracuse University as an art major, but during his freshman year she died of cancer. "She was 49," he says, "a young, beautiful woman." Though Armstrong, enraged and grieving, wanted to drop out, two families who had known his mother took him under their wing, helped him to get scholarships and persuaded him to stay in school. "They took an extraordinary interest in my life," he says. "They forced me to inherit my mom's drive."

Seeking an outlet for his grief, Armstrong, who had drawn cartoon figures for fun since the age of 3, created a grouchy character named Hector, who became a fixture in the *Daily Orange,* the campus newspaper. He also met Sherry West, a chemistry major from Philadelphia, and married her in 1986. "I was saved from a hollow existence by a wonderful woman," he says. "Marriage allowed me to achieve my dreams."

After college, while art director at an ad agency, Armstrong tried to have *Hector* syndicated, only to get a string of rejections. The same thing happened with *Cherry Top,* a strip about a policeman. "If I had known there were only four black syndicated cartoonists in the country, I would have been really discouraged," he says.

Then, in 1988, an editor at United Media in New York City, who had turned down *Cherry Top* because she felt the characters lacked life, asked Armstrong, "Why don't you do something more like yourself?" Within a year, *JumpStart* was off the drawing board and into the funny papers. "I spend all day, every day, thinking about my strip," he says. Twice a month or so, he thinks about it at inner-city schools, where he talks about his unlikely success. "I like giving hope to kids who may be without it," he says.

Working in the studio at his and Sherry's suburban Philadelphia home, Armstrong takes an hour to draw his daily cartoon and three or four to finish his Sunday strip. "He goes through a lot of angst just to get to the point where he can sketch," says Sherry, who designs her own line of sweaters. "These characters," says Armstrong, "really are my kids in a way. I want to treat them right, just like anyone else in my family."

Pancakes

Joan Bauer

The last thing I wanted to see taped to my bathroom mirror at five-thirty in the morning was a newspaper article entitled "Are You a Perfectionist?" But there it was, courtesy of my mother, Ms. Subtlety herself. I was instantly irritated because Allen Feinman had accused me of perfectionism when he broke up with me last month. The term he used was "rabid perfectionism," which I felt was a bit much—but then Allen Feinman had no grip on reality whatsoever. He was rabidly unaware, if the truth be known, like a benign space creature visiting Earth with no interest in going native. I tore the article off the mirror; this left tape smudges. Dirty mirrors drove me crazy. I grabbed the bottle of Windex from the closet and cleaned off the gook until the mirror shined, freed of yellow journalism.[1]

I glowered at the six telltale perfectionist signs in the now crumpled article.

(1) Do you have a driving need to control your environment?

(2) Do you have a driving need to control the environment of others?

(3) Are you miserable when things are out of place?

(4) Are your expectations of yourself and others rarely met?

(5) Do you believe if something is to be done right, only you are the one to do it?

(6) Do you often worry about your performance when it is less than perfect?

1 **yellow journalism:** sensationalized newspaper and magazine stories

Number six had particular sting, for it was that very thing that Allen Feinman had accused me of the day he asked for his green and black lumberjack shirt back, a truly spectacular shirt that looked a lot more spectacular on me than it did on him because it brought out the intensity of my short black hair and my mysterious brown eyes. He had accused me of numbers one through five as well, but on this last fateful day he said, "The problem with you, Jill, is that if the least little thing goes wrong, you can't handle it. Everything has to follow this impossible path to perfection. Someday, and I hope it's soon for your sake, you're going to have to settle for sub-par performance and realize that you're imperfect like the rest of us." He stormed off like an angry prophet who had just delivered a curse, muttering that if I was like this at seventeen, imagine what I would be like at thirty.

"Good riddance," I shouted. "I hope you find a messy, inconsiderate girlfriend who can never find her purse or her car keys, who has no sense of time, no aptitude for *planning,* and that you spend the rest of your adolescent years on your hands and knees looking for your contacts!"

I padded down the hall to my bedroom. It was Sunday morning. I was due at my waitress job at the Ye Olde Pancake House in forty-five minutes. I sat on my white down quilt, saw the chocolate smudge, quick got up and brushed the smudge with my spot remover kit that I kept in my top dresser drawer, being careful to brush the nap against the grain.[2] I put the kit back in the drawer, refluffed my two white pillows, plucked a dead leaf off my philodendron plant, and remembered my second to last fight with Allen when he went completely ballistic at my selfless offer to alphabetize his CD collection with a color-coded cross-reference guide by subject, title, and artist.

Males.

I put on my Ye Olde Pancake House waitress uniform that I had ironed and starched the night before: blue, long-sleeved ankle-length dress, white apron, white-and-blue-flowered bonnet. I could have done without the bonnet, but when you're going for the ye olde look, you have to sacrifice style. I was lucky to have this job. I got it one week after my parents and I moved to town, got hired *because* I am a person of order who knows there is a right way and a wrong way to do things. I replaced a waitress who was a complete disorganized slob. As Howard Halloran, the owner

---

2 **to brush the nap against the grain:** to brush the surface of the fabric against the direction of the threads in the fabric, which helps to remove, rather than set, a stain

of the Ye Olde Pancake House, said to me, "Jill, if you're half as organized and competent as you look, I will die happy." I smoothed back my short clipped hair, flicked a sesame seed off my just-manicured nail, and told him that I was.

"I have a system for everything," I assured him. "Menu first, bring water when you come back to take the order, call it in, bring coffee immediately to follow. Don't ever let customers wait." Then I mentioned my keen knack for alphabetizing condiments, which was always a bonus, particularly when things got busy, and how a restaurant storage closet should be properly organized to take full advantage of the space.

"You're hired," Howard Halloran said reverently, and put me in charge of opening and setting up the restaurant on Saturday and Sunday mornings, which is when nine-tenths of all pancakes in the universe are consumed and you don't want some systemless person at the helm. You want a waitress of grit with a strategic battle plan that never wavers. Sunday morning in a pancake house is war.

I tied my white apron in a perfect bow across my back, tiptoed past my parents' bedroom, taking care not to wake them, even though my mother had taken an insensitive potshot at me without provocation.

It's not like my life had been all that perfect.

Did I ask to move three times in eighteen months because my father kept getting transferred? Did I ask to attend three high schools since sophomore year? Did I complain about being unfairly uprooted?

Well . . . I did complain a little. . . .

Didn't I figure out a way to handle the pressure? When my very roots were being yanked from familiar soil, I became orderly and organized. I did things in the new towns so that people would like me and want to hire me, would want to be my friends. I baked world-class cookies for high school bake sales, even if meant staying up till three A.M.; I joined clubs and volunteered for the grunge jobs that no one wanted; I always turned in a spectacular performance and people counted on me to do it. I made everything look easy. People looked up to me, or down, depending—I'm five four. And I sure didn't feel like defending all that success before dawn!

I tiptoed out the back door to my white Toyota (ancient, yet spotless) and headed for work.

▲ ▲ ▲

Syrup, I tried explaining to Hugo, the busboy, must be poured slowly from the huge cans into the plastic pourers on the tables because if you pour it fast, you can't control the flow and you get syrup everywhere, which never really cleans up. It leaves a sticky residue that always comes back to haunt you. Syrup, I told him, is our enemy, but like Allen Feinman, Hugo was a male without vision. He couldn't anticipate disaster, couldn't cope with forethought and prevention; he let life rule him rather than the other way around, which was why *I* personally filled the syrup containers on Sunday mornings—maple, strawberry, boysenberry, and pecan.

I had just filled the last containers and was putting them on the tables in horizontal rows. I had lined up the juice glasses and coffee mugs for optimal efficiency, which some people who shall remain nameless would call perfectionism, but when the place gets busy, trust me, you want everything at your fingertips or you'll lose control. I never lose control. Hugo had set the back tables and I followed him, straightening the silverware. You'd think he'd been born in a barn. Andy Pappas, the cook, was making the special hash browns with onion and green pepper that people loved.

I steeled myself for the hungry Sunday morning mob that would descend in two hours. I always mentally prepared for situations that I knew were going to be stressful—it helped me handle them right. I could see me, Shirl, and Lucy, the other waitresses, serving the crowd, handling the cash register. Usually Howard Halloran took the money, but he was taking a long-needed weekend off since his wife said if he didn't she would sell the place out from under him. I could see myself watching my station like a hawk, keeping the coffee brewing, getting the pancakes delivered hot to the tables. Do it fast, do it right—that was my specialty.

It was seven o'clock. Shirl and Lucy were late, but I knew that Lucy's baby was sick and Shirl was picking her up, so I didn't worry. They'd been late before. I myself was never late. I unlocked the front door, and a few customers came straggling in with their Sunday newspapers, settling in the booths. Nothing I couldn't handle. Things didn't start getting crazy until around eight-thirty. I had my system.

I took orders, walked quickly to the kitchen window. "Four over easy on eight with sausage," I said crisply. "Side of cakes." That was restaurant-speak for four plates of two eggs over easy with sausage and pancakes on the side. Andy tossed his spatula in the air, went to work. The man had total focus. He could have two dozen eggs cooking in front of him and he knew when to flip each one.

A young family came in with three small children; gave them the big table by the window. Got them kid seats, took their order.

"Number three."

That was my waitress number. Andy called the number over the loud-speaker when my order was ready and I went and picked it up. A nice time-efficient system. I walked quickly to the counter (running made the customers nervous), grabbed the eggs, sausage, and pancakes, carried them four up on my left arm to table six, smiled professionally. Everything all right here, folks? Everyone nodded happily and dug in. Everything was always merry and pleasant at the Ye Olde Pancake House. That's why people came. Merry people left big tips.

I checked the ye olde wall clock. Seven forty-seven. Still no Shirl and Lucy. They'd never been this late. Allen Feinman had been more than an hour late plenty of times. Allen Feinman didn't care about time—his or anyone else's. I didn't understand the grave problems he had at first; I was so caught up in him—this cute, brainy, funny guy who really seemed to want a shot of discipline. I put in my usual extra effort into the relationship—baked his favorite cookies (cappuccino chip), packed romantic picnics (French bread, brie, and strawberries), thought about unusual things to do in Coldwater, Michigan, which was quite a challenge, but I went to the library and came up with a list of ten possible side trips around town that we could do for free.

"You're just so *organized*," he would say, which I thought was a true compliment. Later on, I realized, coming from him, it was the darkest insult.

Andy was flipping pancakes on the grill. I scanned my customers to make sure everyone was cared for, turned to dash into the bathroom quickly when a screech of tires sounded in the parking lot. I looked out the window. A lump caught in my throat.

A large tour bus pulled to a grinding halt.

I watched in horror as an army of round, middle-aged women stepped from the Peter Pan bus[3] and headed toward the restaurant like hungry lionesses stalking prey.

It was natural selection—I was as good as dead.

"Number three."

---

3 **Peter Pan bus:** a bus operated by one of the biggest motorcoach companies in the northeast United States

I looked at Andy, who raised his face to heaven.

"Call them," I shrieked. "Call Shirl and Lucy! Tell them to get here!"

Andy reached for the phone

I turned to the front door as the tour bus women poured in. They were all wearing sweatshirts that read MICHIGAN WOMEN FOR A CLEANER ENVIRONMENT. "A table for sixty-six," said a woman, laughing.

My lungs collapsed. Sixty-six hungry environmentalists. I pointed to a stack of menus, remembering my personal Waitress Rule Number One: Never let a customer know you're out of control.

"Sit anywhere," I cooed. "I'll be right with you."

"If you wrote the menu on a blackboard you wouldn't waste paper," one said.

"Number three." I raced back to the kitchen. Pancakes for table eight. I layered the plates on my left arm, plopped butter balls from the ye olde butter urn on the pancakes. Andy said he'd tried Shirl and Lucy and no one answered. At least they were on their way. I raced to table eight. The little girl took one look at her chocolate chip pancakes and burst into tears.

"They're not the little ones," she sobbed.

"Oh, now, precious," said her father, "I'm sure this nice young lady doesn't want you to be disappointed."

I looked at the environmentalists who needed coffee. Life is tough, kid.

"Tell the waitress what you want, precious."

Precious looked at me, loving the control. She scrunched up her dimples, dabbed her tears, and said, "I want the teeny weeny ones, pwease."

"Teeny weeny ones coming up," I chirped, and raced to Andy. "Chocolate silver dollars for the brat on eight," I snarled. "Make them perfect, or someone dies."

"You're very attractive when you get busy," Andy said laughing.

"Shut up."

The phone rang. I lunged for it. It was Lucy calling from the hospital. Her baby had a bronchial infection, needed medicine. She couldn't come in, but Shirl was on her way, she should be pulling onto the interstate now.

"Are you all right there, Jill?"

"Of course," I lied. "Take care of that baby. That's the most important thing."

"You're terrific," she said, and hung up.

I'm terrific, I told myself. I can handle this because, as a terrific person, I have an organized system that always works. I grabbed two coffee pots and raced to the tour group, smiling. Always smile. Poured coffee. They'd only get water if they asked. We're so glad you came to see us this morning. Yes, we have many tours pass through, usually we have more waitresses, though. It's a safe bet that any restaurant on this earth has more waitresses than the Ye Olde Pancake House does at this moment.

I took their orders like a shotgunner shooting clay pigeons.

Pull!

Pigs in a blanket.

Steak and fried eggs.

Buttermilk pancakes.

Betsy Ross (buttermilks with strawberry and blueberry compote).

Colonial Corn Cakes (Allen Feinman's favorite).

A round-faced woman looked at me, grinning. "Everything looks so good." She sighed. "What do you recommend?"

I recommend that you eat someplace else, ma'am, because I do not have time for this. I looked toward the front of the restaurant; six large men were waiting to be seated. Hugo was pouring syrup quickly into pourers to torture me, sloshing it everywhere. I said, "Everything's great here, ma'am. I'll give you a few seconds to decide." I turned to the woman in the next booth. The round-faced woman grabbed my arm. I don't like being touched by customers.

"Just a minute. Well . . . it all looks so good."

"Number three." I glared in Andy's direction. "And number three again."

A cook can make or break you.

The round-faced woman decided on buttermilk pancakes, a daring choice. I ran to the kitchen window. "Hit me," Andy said.

"I'd love to. You're only getting this once. Buttermilks on twelve. Pigs on four, Betsy's on three. Colonials on seven." I threw the rest of the orders at him.

"You have very small handwriting," he said. "That's often the sign of low self-esteem."

I put my hand down in one of Hugo's syrup spills, pushed back my bangs with it; felt syrup soak my scalp.

Andy said, "You're only one person, Jill."

I scanned the restaurant—juice glasses askew, hungry people waiting at dirty tables. I could do anything if I worked hard enough. Shirl would be here any minute.

"Waitress, we're out of syrup!" A man held his empty syrup container up. I looked under the counter for the extra maple syrup containers I had

cleverly filled, started toward the man, tripped over an environmental-ist's foot, which sent the syrup container flying, caught midair, but upside down by a trucker who watched dumbly as syrup oozed onto the floor in a great, sticky glop. I lunged for the syrup container, slid on the spill, felt sugared muck coat my exposed flesh.

"Hugo!" I screamed, pointing at the disaster. "Hot water!"

"Number three."

I moved in a daze as more and more people came. Got the tour bus groups fed and out. Had they mentioned separate checks, one woman asked?

Noooooooo . . .

Made coffee. More coffee. Told everyone I was the only waitress here, if they were in a hurry, they might want to go someplace else. But no one left. They just kept coming, storming through the restaurant like Cossacks.[4] People were grabbing my arm as I ran by.

"What's your name, babe?" asked a lecherous man.

"*Miss,*" I snarled.

"Number three."

"I had a life when I woke up this morning! Everything was in place!"

Buckwheats on table three. The man looked at them. He said, "You call these buckwheats? Buckwheats are supposed to be enormous and hearty." I'm the fall guy for everything that happens in the restaurant. It's my tip that's floating down the river waving bye-bye. I embraced my personal Waitress Rule Number Two: The customer is always right, even if they're dead wrong. I said, "That's the way we do them here, sir," and he said he can't eat them, he can't look at them, he'll have the buttermilks, not knowing the trouble he's caused me. Andy gets sensitive if someone sends the food back—he's an artist, can't handle criticism. You have to lie to him or he slows down. I raced back to the kitchen.

"The man's a degenerate," I said to Andy. "He wouldn't know a world-class buckwheat if it jumped in his lap. He doesn't deserve to be in the presence of your cooking."

The phone rang. I lunged for it. It's Shirl calling from someone's car phone on the interstate with impossible news. A Coca-Cola trailer truck had jackknifed, spilling cans of diet Coke everywhere. There was a five-mile backup. She'd be hours getting to work.

"Are you all right?" Shirl asked.

---

4 **Cossacks:** the cavalry of the Russian army

I looked at the line of cars pulling into the parking lot, the tables bulging with hungry customers, the coffee cups raised in anticipation of being filled, the line at the cash register. I heard a woman say how the restaurant had gone downhill, and the people were looking at me like I was their breakfast savior, like I had all power and knowing, like I could single-handedly make sure they were happy and fed. And I was ashamed that I couldn't do it, but no one could.

Not even me!

I tore off my ye olde bonnet. "I'm trapped in a pancake house!" I shrieked into the phone, and, like in all sci-fi stories, the connection went dead.

"Number three."

I limped toward him, a shadow of my former self.

"We're out of sausage," Andy said solemnly.

"Good. It's one less thing to carry." I stood on the counter, put my head back, and screamed, "We're out of sausage and it's not my fault!"

A man at a back table hollered that he needed ketchup for his eggs. I reached down in the K section under the counter. Nothing under K. I got on my knees, hands shaking, rifling through jams, jellies, lingonberries.[5] *Hugo!* I shrieked.

He ran up to me.

"Ketchup, Hugo! Wake up! The sky is falling!"

He pointed to the C Section. "Catsup," he said meekly.

I was falling down a dark, disorderly tunnel. There was no end in sight. Coffee grounds were in my eyebrows, my hands smelled like used tea bags. I was exhausted, syrup encrusted, I'd had to go to the bathroom for three hours. People were going to get their own coffee—the ultimate defeat for any waitress. I looked at my haggard reflection in the coffee urn. The only consolation was that I wouldn't live till noon.

"Waitress!" I raced down the aisle to table twelve, seeing the hunted look in my customer's eyes. I wanted to be perfect for every one of you. I wanted you all to like me. I'm sorry I'm not better, not faster. Please don't hate me, I'm only one person, not even a particularly tall person.

"I'm sorry," I said to a table of eight, "but I simply can't do everything!"

I felt a ripple of crass laughter in the air. I turned. Allen Feinman had walked in with his parents.

No, God. Anything but this.

---

5 **lingonberries:** the fruit of the mountain cranberry

Our eyes met. I could hear the taunts at school, the never-ending retelling of this, my ultimate nightmare.

"Can I help, Jill?" He rolled up his shirtsleeves. Allen Feinman was offering to help.

I grabbed his arm. "Can you work the register?"

"Of course." Allen organized the people into a line, made change, smiled. He had such a nice smile. Thanked everyone for their patience, got names on lists.

Mrs. Feinman took off her jacket and asked, "Can I make coffee, dear?"

"Mrs. Feinman, you don't have to—"

"We've always been so fond of you, Jill."

I slapped a bag of decaf in her sainted hands. Mr. Feinman poured himself a cup of coffee and went back to wait in the car.

We shipped that place into shape. All I needed was a little backup. My pockets were bulging with tips, and when Shirl raced in at eleven forty-five, I pushed a little girl aside who'd been waiting patiently by the bathroom door and I lunged toward the toilet stall. Life is tough, kid.

By one-thirty the crowds had cleared. Lucy called—her baby was home and doing better. Allen Feinman and I were sitting at a back table eating pancakes. He said he'd missed me. I said I'd missed him, too. Hugo was speed-pouring boysenberry syrup, spilling everywhere—but somehow it didn't matter anymore. It was good enough.

And that, I realized happily, was fine by me. ∾

Humor Helps

CAROLYN J. GARD

You flunked the world's hardest algebra test. You bang your locker door open. As you're about to stalk off to your next class, your eye catches a cartoon you've taped to your locker door. You laugh all the way to English class.

How did a simple laugh turn your mood completely around?

For years health care professionals have known that stress and anger lead to high blood pressure, muscle tension, and sickness. They weren't sure, however, if the opposite was true. Could humor lower blood pressure and keep people well? The answer is yes. Researchers have found scientific evidence that laughter makes a person feel better.

Studies show that laughter stimulates the immune system by increasing the number and activity of natural killer cells and other antibodies. Laughter also lowers the level of serum cortisol, a substance released by the adrenal gland during stress. In addition, laughing exercises your lungs and increases the amount of oxygen in your blood.

Dr. Peter Derks found that when people listened to jokes, their brain waves spread through their entire cerebral cortex.[1] He concluded that humor uses the whole brain—both the analytical[2] and the sensory[3] parts.

---

1 **cerebral cortex:** the surface layer of the upper part of the brain; it coordinates the senses and movement

2 **analytical:** having to do with thinking or reasoning

3 **sensory:** having to do with the senses

LAUGH IT OFF   A sense of humor isn't an ability—*it's an attitude.*

People who have a good sense of humor are in control of their life and have a lot of self-esteem. That's important, because you can't always control what goes on in your life—you don't write the test questions or decide where your family lives. What you can control is how you react to these events. When you choose to laugh rather than wallow in self-pity, you take control of the situation. Comedian Bill Cosby says, "If you can laugh at it, you can survive it."

Suppose you're the shortest person in your entire school and you're sick and tired of being the brunt of all the short-person jokes. You can get mad at the joke-tellers and storm off, sure that short people have no chance of success in the world. Or you can respond with a witty remark and get on to another subject.

The first response simply makes you madder. The second response disarms your tormentors. By laughing at yourself, you've become powerful. You don't let others define who you are.

Kinds of Humor   A sense of humor doesn't mean laughing at everything.

Most humor has one of three targets—yourself, a situation, or another person. When you laugh at yourself, you make those around you feel safe.

Joking about humorous situations, such as what happened when the lights went out at the dance, keeps the target of the joke away from others. The worst kind of humor—and the one to avoid—is humor directed at others. This includes sarcasm, put-downs, and jokes that are insensitive to the feelings of others.

Healthy humor brings people together. Telling a joke about a familiar experience gives people a sense of belonging, of being part of the group.

Now, That's Funny!   While laughter seems to come more easily to some people than to others, most of us probably had a good sense of humor when we were young. One study found that the average kindergartner laughs 300 times a day, while the average adult laughs only 17 times a day. You don't want to outgrow your ability to laugh.

Listen to yourself to see what you laugh at. Then collect books, magazines, comics, and videos that reinforce your sense of humor. When you don't think you can cram another fact into your head, take a humor break. You'll come back to your project refreshed, and just possibly, with a new killer idea.

As you learn to laugh at yourself, you enhance your self-esteem. You relax, and you laugh more. As you laugh more, you become more fun to be with, and you'll have the wonderful dilemma of being too much in demand. ∾

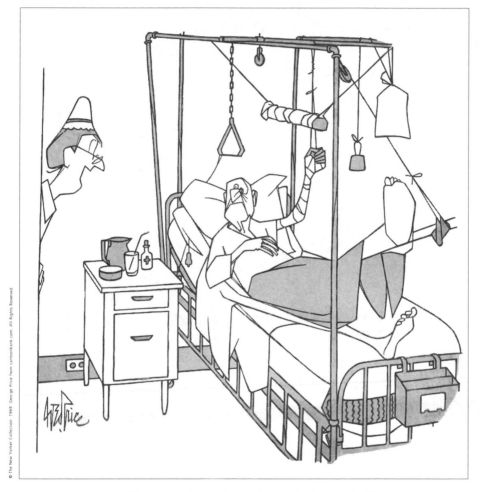

"Have your pillows been plumped this morning?"

Money:

Too Tight to Mention

SINBAD

In the following selection, stand-up comic Sinbad remembers what it was like to grow up in a large and loving family in which money was tight.

Can you pay for it? That's the number one question. Get a job, fall in love, buy a house, buy a car; it's the same—you got what it takes? And how are you gonna pay? Cash, credit, layaway?[1] Layaway I've hated since I was small. Go to the store, pick out the cool pair of pants, know you're looking good. Then you go to pay, and Mama's messed you up: "Here's ten dollars down, and we'll put a dollar in a week."

A dollar a week? It can take a whole life to pay off that layaway. You visit your clothes and watch them go out of style. Then, fifty-five years old—"I'm picking up the burgundy sharkskin[2] pants, boys' size six."

Layaway tickets handed down for generations! Folks even leave a layaway ticket in the will, like it's some kind of family heirloom. Like I'm actually going to Kmart with the layaway ticket to pick up that pair of slippery-sliders, the kind of shoes get you killed playing dodge ball.

Still, layaway clothes were a luxury in my family. Six kids—my mama would sew, and those clothes were made to last. Two suits in one: powder

1 **layaway:** a system that allows customers to pay in installments for items that are kept at the store until all payments are made

2 **sharkskin:** a smooth fabric with a dull shine that was popular in the seventies but generally considered outdated today

blue on the outside; and when it got dirty, inside there was purple plaid. No zipper—just a strip of Velcro to get old and fuzzy and then you'd stand up in class and your pants would pop open. Girls laughing: "Ooh, he's wearing Spiderman underpants." I was eighteen years old at the time . . .

I'm a father now, so I know kids' feet grow at least an inch a day, and I can understand how hard my parents worked to keep us in shoes. But as a child I used to dread our trips to Kmart—the six of us crowding the bargain table, where all the shoes were tied together on one long string. Like, "Don't let them get loose or they'll stampede." Mama would tell us, "Now, this time, only two of y'all are getting shoes." And I'd pray, "Please, not me!" Those shoes were too tough to bend or crease; they'd defend your feet like steel or wooden shields. You could walk through fire in them and never feel a thing, but you'd be walking like Frankenstein— that's how tight they squeezed.

Tight as they were, they couldn't hold on to our tube socks, the kind that cost a dollar for a hundred pair. Soon as you pulled them up, the elastic in those socks would explode, so they'd roll off your feet and jump right out of the shoe! Remember all those socks you'd see on the curb when we were kids? They'd all jumped off people's feet and got washed down to the gutter when it rained.

At least those cheap clothes and shoes and socks were new, not just "new to you" like a lot of our stuff. In the Midwest when I was growing up, rummage sales[3] were the key to life. In California—drive up in the Mercedes-Benz, play like they're looking for antiques—folks like to call them "estate sales." Who are they trying to fool? If there's a piece of cardboard nailed to the light pole, with an arrow pointing to your house, it's a rummage sale: You need some money, we need your old stuff.

My mother is Benton Harbor's Golden Gloves champion[4] of the rummage sales. She's gentle and sweet, a preacher's wife, but she can take care of business. Some women train for rummage sales—weight lifting, kick boxing—but not my mama; after raising six kids, she thought gyms were for amateurs. I've seen her kung-fu fight for a cashmere coat— whup twenty women, get that coat to the table, then power-bargain, not

---

3 **rummage sales:** like garage sales, these are events in which unwanted items are sold, usually inexpensively and usually from private homes

4 **Benton Harbor's Golden Gloves champion:** Benton Harbor, Michigan, is the author's hometown; the Golden Gloves champion is the winner of a well-known boxing competition.

even catching her breath. "Ten dollars! Why, this isn't worth five. I'll give you three . . . Not seven, three-fifty . . ."

The other women are all still gasping on the ground. I'd get so embarrassed that I'd pull out the dollar I'd made from cashing in bottles. "Here, Mama, please pay her four-fifty and let's leave."

"I'm not paying a penny more than three seventy-five . . ." She was tough.

And fast. The second she heard, "There's a better sale on Robin Street," she would haul butt, cutting down the alleys and switching back to ditch the competition. She was one of those queens of the rummage sales—when she showed up, you knew that your sale was a good one. Friday night was when the signs would get tacked to the telephone poles, and my mother would drive around trying to sniff them out. We'd be sitting in the back of the station wagon and we'd see that familiar piece of cardboard tacked to a pole, and we'd be praying: "Please, don't let Mama see it." But my mama wouldn't miss it. She had excellent rummage sale peripheral vision—she could see 180 degrees behind her without using the rearview mirror. *Screeeech*—she's stopped the car, she's backing up. "What does that say?"

"Mama, I can't read it, it's too dark out."

"You will read that sign . . ."

It got so on Saturdays other women would stake out our street, sitting there at dawn on our lawn with their motors idling, watching for my mother to make her move.

The worst thing was, she made us all go to the sales with her. Then you might as well say good-bye to your pride. Right in the backyard, she'd toss you some pants: "Here, try these on."

"Where?"

"Just take off your pants. Hurry up."

"Mama . . ."

"You've got nothing for anyone to see."

"Thanks, tell the world . . ."

I'm standing there in my rummage-sale Spiderman underwear, a station wagon pulls up—"Look at him!"—kids are laughing. And I know I can never go back to school again.

That taught me a lesson: to jump out while Mama was parking the car and get to the sale first. She was surprised, but I lied and told her I liked shopping. Mama, let me finally confess the truth, here and now: I was running around finding everything that would fit me so I could hide it from you.

The worst rummage sale item she ever got me was a pair of green Adidas.[5] All I'd ever seen was white Adidas, so I thought they were super-cool. She was proud too: "You don't find too many pairs of size thirteen shoes for fifty cents." But when I wore them to basketball practice, I kept smelling fumes and the green seemed to be cracking. Someone had spray-painted those shoes.

Then one of my teammates came up to me: "Hey, those are my shoes! Where'd you get them?"

"Uh, my mama found them someplace and wanted me to get them back to you."

"I don't want them. I threw them out."

"You did? Here they are anyway." And I walked home barefoot, my head hanging low.

My mother was a trashpicker too. She actually took an upholstery class in case she spotted some "antique" out on the curb, so she could take it home and fix it. In the eighties she upgraded to bungee cord, but when I was young we always carried clothesline with us in case something didn't fit, so we could tie the trunk shut or rope it to the top of the car. One time, she found a couch. "Let's just take it," I said, but no—she forced me to get out of the car and ring the doorbell. "Uh, hello, my mother wants to know if we can have that couch out of your trash . . ."

The woman thought we were so pitiful: "Oh, we're throwing out some tables and a chair too . . ."

"No! No! We just want the couch!"

Now I know what I should have done: Rung that bell and when the woman answered, said, "My mother thinks that couch in your trash is the ugliest thing she's ever seen. Get it off the street, or else we're calling the police."

▲ ▲ ▲

My father had a different approach to thrift. He was the fixingest man you've ever seen. If Mama found something broken at a rummage sale, she'd reserve it for my daddy with her "swoop back" technique. Like a TV— in the morning, Mama would say she was interested just to get the man's hopes up, then all day he'd be expecting someone to meet his price. Right when the sale was closing, Mama would swoop back—"Oh, I see you've still got that old TV. Well, it's still not worth twenty dollars." By then

5 **Adidas:** a brand of running shoe

the man would let her have it for five dollars rather than haul it back in the garage. And within a few days, my daddy would have it up and running, having spent only fifty dollars to fix it. Then we'd have to hear the story over and over again—on how he and only he could have saved that TV set.

One time my sister totaled the car; it hit a gas pump and blew up. But even though he got the insurance money, my father towed the car back home. He had to buy sheet metal, but he rebuilt that car—he just couldn't let it go to waste. Sometimes we resented his ability to fix things. I had a cool-looking bike—purple Sting Ray, with big handlebars and a yellow banana seat—but it was cheap. Every couple months, the handlebars popped off. Almost got me killed. But my father just kept welding those handlebars back on until the bike was nothing but one big gray weld— "Look out! Big lump of solder[6] rolling down the street!" Folks would scream and jump out of the way. The only thing on it that still looked like a bike was the banana seat.

▲ ▲ ▲

I feel lucky that my parents were thrifty. Because of rummage sales and my dad's fix-it capability, I could wear cool clothes and have things that a family at our income level wouldn't usually have. Early on I learned to bargain and to fix things. And I must admit that every now and then I use the swoop-back technique to see if it still works. Those old habits die hard.

But, hey, it was tough asking thrifty parents for money. You've got to beg fathers: "Dad, can I have a dollar?"

"What happened to the dollar I gave you last year?" and then get the lecture: "Boy, let me tell you something. Money doesn't grow on trees . . ."

You have to act like, "Oh, man, I didn't know that," when what you want to say is, "If it did, I'd be outside picking it, not in here fighting with you."

Mothers will cry when you ask for money, but they'll always try to give it to you. "Mama, I need $500."

"Oh, child, here, take it, don't worry about us—we'll just bounce our check to the landlord. Pray we don't get evicted or go to jail . . ." You feel bad.

The best person to ask for money is your grandmother. Grandmothers always have money—no job, haven't worked in fifty years—it's like God puts magic money in their purses. "Grandma, I need $2,000."

"Let me just look in my pocketbook . . . Oh, here's $2,500. Buy yourself a treat . . ." ∾

6 **solder:** a soft, easily melted metal that is used to join two or more pieces of metal

RESPONDING TO CLUSTER TWO

HOW IS HUMOR USED?

Thinking Skill ANALYZING

1. The kids in the story "Fish Eyes" outdo each other with practical jokes. Imagine that Jill from "Pancakes" visits this family. How do you think she would get along? Use **analysis** to explain your response. (Analysis is when you break a subject into parts and examine each part.)

2. In the cartoon strip "JumpStart," cartoonist Robb Armstrong uses gentle humor to illustrate family life. Choose a favorite scene or incident from a story in this cluster and draw a cartoon strip that tells the story.

3. Choose the sentence in "Humor Helps" that best reflects your ideas about humor. Explain your choice.

4. Using the Laugh-O-Meter chart you began in Cluster One, rank the humor quotient of the stories in this cluster.

5. Some readers may believe that in "Money: Too Tight To Mention" Sinbad makes fun of poor people. Do you agree or disagree? Why?

Writing Activity: Analyzing the Uses of Humor

In most humor, there is an underlying purpose. For example in Cluster 1, Dave Barry uses humor in "Memories of Dating" to soften the humiliations and uncertainties of dating. In a sentence each, explain what you think the authors' purposes were in writing the selections in this cluster.

To Analyze Purpose

- decide what the subject is
- determine what the author's attitude toward the subject is (for example, mocking, playful or serious)
- decide what the point of the piece would be if the author was writing seriously instead of humorously
- take all of the above factors into account and summarize what you think the author's purpose is

CLUSTER THREE

What Are Some Types of Humor?

Thinking Skill   CLASSIFYING

The original scarier version of Star Wars

"MAKES YA THINK."

Blue

THINK

THE FAR SIDE

By GARY LARSON

"What are you gonna tell your dad?"

Youngest Child
Tries to Tell a Joke

Erma Bombeck

Our youngest child has been trying to tell a joke at the dinner table for the last three years. The same one.

I feel sorry for the kid. To be on the tail end of a family means anything you come up with has either been told or isn't worth telling. We can always tell when his favorite magazine comes in the mail. He will rush into the kitchen and say, "Why did it take three Boy Scouts to help a little old lady across the street?" and one of the older ones will shout, "Because she didn't want to go, you cluck!"

Personally I wish he'd take the magazine, crumple it and stuff it in every opening in his face, but he never does. He always looks amazed that someone knew the answer and says, "That's right."

Next month, it's the same old deal. "How do you stop an elephant from charging?" His sister, looking bored, will snap, "Let me guess. You take away his credit cards."

"That's right," he says, perplexed.

About three years ago he said, "Have you heard the story about a man who bought a mousetrap and went to the refrigerator for cheese and—"

"Which reminds me," interrupted his father. "Who ate the beer cheese?"

"I didn't eat it," one of the kids said. "I used it for bass bait."

In the months to follow, we were to hear the preamble to the joke dozens of times . . . always with interruptions, never completed.

Finally, one day last week I said, "Tell me your joke about the man with the mousetrap and the cheese for bait."

"Well," he said, perching himself on the stool, "he found out he didn't have any cheese for bait, so he cut a picture from a magazine of a piece of cheese. When he woke up the next morning, know what he found in his trap? A picture of a mouse."

"Tell it at dinner," I urged.

Under protest, the family sat rigid and listened to the story without interruption. By the time he got to his punch line he was hysterical. His eyes were shining with excitement, and I thought he was going to explode as he built for his big finish. "And do you know what he found in this trap?" he asked. *"A mouse!"*

No one said a word. I wonder whether Henny Youngman[1] got started this way. ∾

1 **Henny Youngman:** an American comedian of the sixties

Word Wit

Yogi-isms
(comments attributed to Yankee catcher Yogi Berra)

Sometimes you can observe a lot by watching.

No wonder nobody comes here—it's too crowded.

A nickel ain't worth a dime anymore.

Half the lies they tell me aren't true.

When you come to the fork in the road, take it.

It ain't over 'til it's over.

If the people don't want to come out to the park,
nobody's going to stop 'em.

Tom Swifties

You make a Tom Swifty by writing a sentence of dialogue in which the adverb (the word that tells how you say or do something) creates a pun.

"In fact, those birds aren't swallows," said Tom *swiftly*.

"Don't you love sleeping outdoors?" Tom asked *intently*.

"Have you seen the ring I gave Mary?" Tom asked *engagingly*.

"Try that direction," Tom suggested *pointedly*.

"I'm willing to risk catching the Plague," Tom said *rashly*.

"I just can't remember what Mother asked me to buy,"
Tom mumbled *listlessly*.

"Just connect this terminal and I'm sure the light'll work,"
Tom said *positively*.

"The thermostat is set too high," Tom said *heatedly*.

Croakers

Croakers are similar to Tom Swifties except that they use a verb instead of an adverb to make the pun.

"I'm dying," she *croaked*.

"Someone's at the door," he *chimed*.

"Drowning's no laughing matter," she *gurgled*.

"J.R. made wads of money in oil," he *gushed*.

"I will correct your math," she *added*.

"I ordered chocolate, not vanilla," I *screamed*.

Actual Headlines

10 REVOLTING OFFICERS EXECUTED

TOWN TO DROP SCHOOL BUS WHEN OVERPASS IS READY

FARMER BILL DIES IN HOUSE

HERSHEY BARS PROTEST

Excuses, Excuses (from parents to schools)

Please excuse Roland from P.E. for a few days.
Yesterday he fell out of a tree
and misplaced his hip.

John has been absent because he had two
teeth taken off his face.

Chris will not be in school cus he has an acre in his side.

Sally won't be in school a week from Friday.
We have to attend a funeral.

Silly Signs

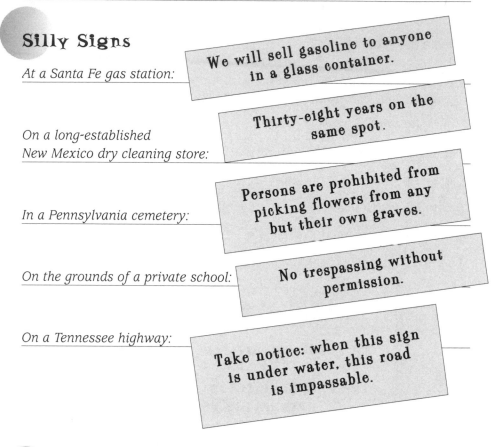

At a Santa Fe gas station:

> We will sell gasoline to anyone in a glass container.

On a long-established New Mexico dry cleaning store:

> Thirty-eight years on the same spot.

In a Pennsylvania cemetery:

> Persons are prohibited from picking flowers from any but their own graves.

On the grounds of a private school:

> No trespassing without permission.

On a Tennessee highway:

> Take notice: when this sign is under water, this road is impassable.

Sniglets

When there is no word in the dictionary to express what you mean, make one up! The result is a sniglet.

BURGACIDE (burg' uh side)
n. When a hamburger can't take any more torture and hurls itself through the grill into the coals.

CARPERPETUATION (kar' pur pet u a shun)
n. The act, when vacuuming, of running over a string or a piece of lint at least a dozen times, reaching over and picking it up, examining it, then putting it back down to give the vacuum one more chance.

ELBONICS (el bon' iks)

n. The actions of two people maneuvering for one armrest in a movie theater.

ELECELLERATION (el a cel er a' shun)

n. The mistaken notion that the more you press an elevator button the faster it will arrive.

FRUST (frust)

n. The small line of debris that refuses to be swept onto the dust pan and keeps backing a person across the room until he finally decides to give up and sweep it under the rug.

NEONPHANCY (ne on' fan see)

n. A fluorescent light bulb struggling to come to life.

PHONESIA (fo nee' zhuh)

n. The affliction of dialing a phone number and forgetting whom you were calling just as they answer.

PUPKUS (pup' kus)

n. The moist residue left on a window after a dog presses its nose to it.

Jokes

Q. What do prisoners use to call each other?
A. *Cell phones.*

Q. What do you get from a pampered cow?
A. *Spoiled milk.*

Q. Where do polar bears vote?
A. *The North Poll.*

Q. Why do seagulls fly over the sea?
A. *Because if they flew over the bay they would be bagels.*

Q. Why did the tomato blush?
A. *Because it saw the salad dressing.*

Q. How do you make a tissue dance?
A. *Put a little boogey in it!*

Q. What did the judge say when the skunk walked in the court room?
A. *Odor in the court.*

Q. What would you get if you crossed a dinosaur with a pig?
A. *Jurassic pork.*

Q. How do you get a longhaired cat to come to the phone?
A. *Make a Persian-to-Persian call.*

Q. What do you call a lazy toy?
A. *An inaction figure.*

Q. What are the most athletic rodents?
A. *Track and field mice.*

Q. What did the spider do on the computer?
A. *Made a website!*

Q. What do you call a cheese that is not yours?
A. *Nacho cheese.*

First Grade Proverbs

A first grade teacher gave the children in her class the first half of several proverbs and had them come up with the rest.

Better Be Safe Than . . . *Punch a 7th Grader.*

Strike While The . . . *Bug is Close.*

It's Always Darkest Before . . . *Daylight Savings Time.*

Don't Bite The Hand That . . . *Looks Dirty.*

A Miss Is As Good As A . . . *Mr.*

You Can't Teach An Old Dog New . . . *Math.*

If You Lie Down With Dogs, You'll . . . *Stink In The Morning.*

An Idle Mind Is . . . *The Best Way to Relax.*

Where There's Smoke, There's . . . *Pollution.*

Happy The Bride Who . . . *Gets All The Presents.*

A Penny Saved Is . . . *Not Much.*

I Wish I'd Said That

There are three kinds of people: those who can count and those who can't.

Why is "abbreviation" such a long word?

For people who like peace and quiet: a phoneless cord.

Proofread carefully to see if you any words out.

If at first you DO succeed, try not to look astonished.

If things get any worse, I'll have to ask you to stop helping me.

Copywight 1999 Elmer Fudd. All wights wesewved.

I think animal testing is a terrible idea; they get all nervous and give the wrong answers.

Time's fun when you're having flies (Kermit the Frog).

Punny Stuff

Two paddlers sitting in a kayak were chilly; but when they lit a fire in the craft, it sank, proving once and for all that you can't have your kayak and heat it too.

> Two atoms are walking down the street and they run into each other. One says to the other, "Are you all right?"
> "No, I lost an electron!"
> "Are you sure?"
> "Yeah, I'm positive."

A group of chess enthusiasts checked into a hotel and were standing on the mezzanine above the lobby discussing their recent tournament victories. After about an hour, the manager came out of the office and asked them to disperse. "But why?" they asked as they moved off. "Because," he said, "I can't stand chess nuts boasting in an open foyer."

> A man entered a local paper's pun contest. He sent in ten different puns in the hope that at least one of the puns would win.
> No pun in ten did.

The Clown

PATRICK F. MCMANUS

I admit it: my sense of humor is a bit weird. It's caused me some trouble over the years. For example, the only time I ever got sent to the principal's office at Delmore Blight Junior High was because I laughed in the wrong place at the wrong time—Miss Bindle's math class.

They don't make teachers like Miss Bindle anymore. At least, I hope they don't. She was tiny, scrawny, and fierce, with an eighty-year-old face and twenty-year-old red hair. Her wrinkles were permanently fused into a frown beneath the glowing halo of frizzy hair. Miss Bindle was the Jesse James of sarcasm: she could quick-draw a sarcastic remark and drill you between the eyes with it at thirty paces. She once hit Mort Simmons with a slug of sarcasm that spun him around half out of his desk. Then she walked over and coolly finished him off with two shots to the head. Mort recovered, but he was never the same afterward. His was a sad case.

Mort had always been dumb. The reason Miss Bindle drilled him was that he had been sneaking a look at one of my answers during a test; that's how dumb he was, or so Miss Bindle remarked, catching me with a ricochet from her shot at Mort. She never coddled us dumb kids, as did some of the kinder, more merciful teachers. She made us learn the same stuff as the smart kids. A few teachers took pity on us and let us relax in the cozy vacuum of our dumbness, but Miss Bindle forced us to learn everything the smart kids did, even though it took us three times as long. Everybody hated her for it, even the smart kids, who were cheated out of the satisfaction of knowing more than the dumb ones. Anybody could see that wasn't fair.

But I started to tell about Mort. He couldn't do arithmetic without counting on his fingers. Miss Bindle said she didn't care what parts of his anatomy he had to count on, he was going to learn just as much math as anybody else. Mort did, too, but it was a terrible strain on him, dumb as he was. When we got to multiplying and dividing fractions, his fingers moved so fast he had to keep a glass of ice water on his desk to cool them off. It was a good thing we didn't do algebra in seventh grade, because somebody would have had to stand next to Mort with a fire extinguisher.

It is my understanding that modern educational theory dismisses the use of fear as a means of inducing learning in adolescents. Educators now take a more civilized approach and try to make learning an enjoyable experience. I agree with that. I know that all my children enjoyed school much more than I did. On the other hand, none of them knows how to multiply and divide fractions. I suppose that's part of the trade-off.

▲　▲　▲

Fear was Miss Bindle's one and only motivator. It was as though she had done her teacher training at Marine boot camp. She would stick her face an inch from yours and, snarling and snapping, rearrange the molecules of your brain to suit her fancy. It was clearly evident to the person whose brain molecules were being rearranged that breath mints either hadn't been invented or hadn't come in a flavor pleasing to Miss Bindle. The oral hygiene of an executioner, however, is scarcely a matter of great concern to the potential victim.

Miss Bindle preferred psychological violence—whipping your psyche[1] into a pink froth—to physical violence. Physical violence was direct and straightforward, something all of us youngsters thoroughly understood. There was no mystery to it. Given a choice, we would have taken the teacher's physical violence, which consisted of snatching the culprit by the hair and dragging him off to the principal's office. As I say, Miss Bindle was extremely short, only about half the size of some of the larger boys. When Miss Bindle grabbed them by the hair and took off for the office, they had to trail along behind her in a bent-over posture, which didn't do a lot for the macho[2] image of some of the guys, particularly if they were saying, "Ow ow ow," as they went out the door. On the other

---

1 **psyche:** the soul, self, and mind
2 **macho:** exaggeratedly masculine

hand, if they had stood erect, in order to depart from the room in a dignified fashion, Miss Bindle would have dangled from their hair, her feet swinging a good six inches off the floor. It was a no-win situation, and wisdom dictated the less painful of the two modes of being escorted to the office. In contrast to Miss Bindle, other teachers merely pointed toward the door and ordered, "Go to the office!" This method allowed the typical louts,[3] some of whom were near voting age, to leave the room swaggering and sneering. No lout ever left Miss Bindle's room swaggering and sneering.

I was a fairly timid fellow and took great care never to attract the wrath of Miss Bindle. I studied ways to make myself invisible in her class, with such success that a couple of times she marked me absent when I was there. Pitiful victims were snatched from their desks on all sides of me, but month after month I escaped unsnatched, making myself increasingly invisible, until finally there were only a few weeks left of my seventh-grade sentence. I thought I was going to make it safely through to the end of the school year, but I hadn't taken into account my weird sense of humor—or my friend Slick.

Clifford Slick was the class clown. Ol' Slick felt his purpose in life was to make people laugh, and he was pretty good at it. Everybody liked Slick. We would gather around him during lunch hour to watch his routines and laugh ourselves sick. He did a wonderful impression of Miss Bindle snatching a kid by the hair and dragging him off. He did both parts alternately, the kid and Miss Bindle, and it was hilarious. One of the reasons Slick got the routine down so well was that he got snatched about once a week. It was as though he had researched the act. He knew every little nuance[4] of a snatching, and how to exaggerate it just enough to turn the horror into humor. It was a gift.

One day before school, I made the mistake of bragging to Slick that I was going to make it all the way through the year without getting snatched by Miss Bindle. Slick was concentrating on combing his hair into a weird shape. His father had shot a bear, and Slick had come into a quantity of bear grease. He slathered a copious amount of bear grease on his hair and was delighted to see that he could now comb it into any shape he wanted. He combed it flat down against his skull, so that it looked as though he were wearing a shiny, tight leather helmet.

3 **louts:** crude or slow people
4 **nuance:** a slight or subtle variation

"How's that look?" he asked me. "Funny?"

I grinned. "Yeah, pretty funny, Cliff. I like the one best, though, where you comb it straight out from your forehead. It looks like a duck bill. Ha!"

"Okay, good," he said. "I'll go with that. Should get some laughs. Now what was that you were saying?"

"I said I've never been snatched by Miss Bindle. I'm going to make it all the way through the year without getting snatched."

Slick turned a malevolent smile on me. "No you ain't. Today you're going to bust out laughing right in old Bindle's class!"

"Not a chance!" The mere thought of bursting out laughing in Miss Bindle's class would totally paralyze my entire laughing apparatus. It was like having a fail-safe mechanism.

"You'll laugh," Slick said. "I'll make you laugh."

I shook my head. "No way."

In the whole hundred or so years that Miss Bindle had taught, I was reasonably sure that not so much as a snicker had ever been heard in her class, let alone a laugh. It was absolutely insane for Slick to think that I, a profoundly fearful and insecure person, would achieve fame as the one kid ever to burst out laughing within snatching range of Miss Bindle.

▲ ▲ ▲

As soon as Miss Bindle's back was turned to scratch some fractions on the blackboard, Slick went into his routine. He took a dainty sip from his ink bottle and then made a terrible face. His greasy duck-bill hair contributed considerably to the comedy. I felt a laugh coming on but easily strangled it. Slick looked disappointed. Then he stuck two yellow pencils up his nose, his impression of a walrus. I felt a major laugh inflating inside me. Slick next imitated a walrus taking a dainty sip of tea. That almost got me, but the laugh exploded deep in my interior with a muffled *whump!* Suspicious, Olga Bonemarrow, in the next row, glared at me. Feeling as though I had suffered major internal injuries, I wiped some tears from my eyes. Slick took this as an encouraging sign and pulled out all the stops. He was doing his duck-bill walrus daintily sipping tea while wiggling its ears when Miss Bindle turned to face the class.

"Clifford!" she roared, hurtling down the aisle like a tiny, ancient, red-headed dreadnought.[5] Slick's ears ceased to wiggle; the pencils in his nose quivered; a bit of inky drool dribbled from his gaping mouth. He

5 **dreadnought:** a powerful battleship

clenched his eyes in preparation for a major-league snatching. Miss Bindle grabbed at his hair and headed off down the aisle, obviously expecting Slick to be firmly in tow. But Slick was still seated at his desk, eyes clenched, pencils up nose. Miss Bindle rushed back and made another pass at his hair, but again her hand slipped off. She snatched again and again, with even less effect. Apparently, it was the first time she had ever encountered bear-greased hair on one of her snatchees.

All the while, Slick sat there numbly, the yellow pencils poking out of his nose and a terrible expression on his face. Maybe it was Slick's expression that got to me, or maybe it was the way the teacher stared down at her greasy palms, her eyes full of rage and disgust and incomprehension. Whatever the trigger, it bypassed the fail-safe mechanism. My wild, booming laugh detonated like a bomb in the frozen silence of the room. I could scarcely believe it was my own laugh. I hoped it might be Mort's: only he might possibly be stupid enough to laugh in Miss Bindle's math class. But no, the laugh, now diminishing from a roar into a sort of breathless squealing, was none other than my own. I had been betrayed by my weird sense of humor! By Clifford Slick and his bear grease! And yes, even by Miss Bindle! As I writhed in an agony of mirth, half hilarity and half terror, I could feel Miss Bindle's stiletto[6] eyes piercing my living—for the moment—flesh. My stunned classmates failed to find my laughter infectious. He who laughed in Miss Bindle's class laughed alone.

And then it happened. "Clifford! Pat!" snarled Miss Bindle. "Go to the office!" She pointed the way with a finger shiny with bear grease.

I left the classroom erect and dignified. Cliff went out the door sideways, doing his comical little vaudeville dance. It didn't get a laugh.

After the principal, Mr. Wiggens, gave us his bored lecture on the importance of discipline in a learning environment, he ordered us back to class. As I was passing the entrance of the cloakroom, I heard strange sounds emanating from the far end. A quick glance revealed that it was Miss Bindle. At first I thought she was crying, possibly over the disappointment of failing to snatch Cliff's and my hair. But no! She was laughing! Cackling, actually, quietly and to herself. It struck me that Miss Bindle had a weird sense of humor, too. ❧

---

6 **stiletto:** a slender dagger with a very sharp point

Hey, You Down There!

HAROLD ROLSETH

Calvin Spender drained his coffee cup and wiped his mouth with the back of his hand. He belched loudly and then proceeded to fill a corncob pipe with coarsely shredded tobacco. He scratched a match across the top of the table and, holding it to his pipe, he sucked noisily until billows of acrid smoke poured from his mouth.

Dora Spender sat across the table from her husband, her breakfast scarcely touched. She coughed lightly, and then, as no frown appeared on Calvin's brow, she said, "Are you going to dig in the well this morning, Calvin?"

Calvin fixed his small red-rimmed eyes upon her and, as if she had not spoken, said, "Git going at the chores right away. You're going to be hauling up dirt."

"Yes, Calvin," Dora whispered. Calvin cleared his throat, and the action caused his Adam's apple to move convulsively under the loose red folds of skin on his neck. He rose from the table and went out the kitchen door, kicking viciously at the tawny cat which had been lying on the doorstep.

Dora gazed after him and wondered for the thousandth time what it was that Calvin reminded her of. It was not some other person. It was something else. Sometimes it seemed as though the answer was about to spring to her mind, as just now when Calvin had cleared his throat. But always it stopped just short of her consciousness. It was disturbing to know with such certainty that Calvin looked like something other than himself and yet not know what that something was. Someday though, Dora knew, the answer would come to her. She rose hurriedly from the table and set about her chores.

Half-way between the house and the barn a doughnut-shaped mound of earth surrounded a hole. Calvin went to the edge of the hole and stared down into it distastefully. Only necessity could have forced him to undertake this task, but it was either this digging or the hauling of barrels and barrels of water each day from Nord Fisher's farm a half mile down the road.

Calvin's herd of scrub cattle was small, but the amount of water it consumed was astonishing. For two weeks now, ever since his well had gone dry, Calvin had been hauling water, and the disagreeable chore was becoming more unpleasant because of neighbour Nord's clumsy hints that some form of payment for the water would not be amiss.

Several feet back from the edge of the hole Calvin had driven a heavy iron stake into the ground, and to this was attached a crude rope ladder. The rope ladder had become necessary when the hole had reached a depth well beyond the length of any wooden ladder Calvin owned.

Calvin hoped desperately that he would not have to go much deeper. He estimated that he was now down fifty or sixty feet, a common depth for many wells in the area. His greatest fear was that he would hit a stratum of rock which would call for the services of a well-drilling outfit. For such a venture both his funds and his credit rating were far too low.

Calvin picked up a bucket to which was attached a long rope and lowered it into the hole. It was Dora's backbreaking task to haul the bucket up hand over hand after Calvin had filled it from the bottom of the hole.

With a mumbled curse Calvin emptied his pipe and started down the rope ladder. By the time he got to the bottom of the hole and had filled the bucket, Dora should be there to haul it up. If she weren't, she would hear about it.

From the house Dora saw Calvin prepare to enter the well, and she worked with desperate haste to complete her chores. She reached the hole just as a muffled shout from below indicated that the bucket was full.

Summoning all her strength, Dora hauled the bucket up. She emptied it and then lowered it into the hole again. While she waited for the second bucketload, she examined the contents of the first. She was disappointed to find it had only the normal moistness of underground earth. No water seeped from it.

In her own fashion, Dora was deeply religious and at each tenth bucket she pulled up she murmured an urgent prayer that it would contain more water in it than earth. She had settled at praying at every tenth bucketload because she did not believe it in good taste to pester God with every bucket. Also, she varied the wording of each prayer, feeling that God must become bored with the same petition repeated over and over.

On this particular morning as she lowered the bucket for its tenth loading, she prayed, "Please God, let something happen this time . . . let something really and truly happen so I won't have to haul up any more dirt."

Something happened almost immediately. As the rope slackened in her hands indicating that the bucket had reached the bottom, a scream of sheer terror came up from the hole, and the rope ladder jerked violently. Whimpering sounds of mortal fear sounded faintly, and the ladder grew taut with heavy strain.

Dora fell to her knees and peered down into the darkness. "Calvin," she called, "are you all right? What is it?"

Then, with startling suddenness, Calvin appeared, literally shooting out of the hole. At first Dora was not sure it was Calvin. The peeled redness of his face was gone; now it was a yellowish green. He was trembling violently and had trouble breathing.

It must be a heart attack, Dora thought, and tried mightily to suppress the surge of joy that swept over her.

Calvin lay upon the ground panting. Finally he gained control of himself. Under ordinary circumstances Calvin did not converse with Dora, but now he seemed eager to talk. "You know what happened down there?" he said in a shaky voice. "You know what happened? The complete bottom dropped right out of that hole. All of a sudden it went, and there I was, standing on nothing but air. If I hadn't grabbed aholt of the last rung of the ladder . . . Why, that hole must be a thousand feet the way the bottom dropped out of it!"

Calvin babbled on, but Dora did not listen. She was filled with awe at the remarkable way in which her prayer had been answered. If the hole had no more bottom, there would be no more dirt to haul up.

When Calvin had regained his strength, he crept to the edge of the hole and peered down.

"What are you going to do, Calvin?" Dora asked timidly.

"Do? I'm going to find out how far down that hole goes. Get the flashlight from the kitchen."

Dora hurried off. When she returned, Calvin had a large ball of binder twine[1] he had gotten from the tool shed.

---

1 **binder twine:** a strong string used to tie things together

He tied the flashlight securely to the end of the line, switched it on, and lowered it into the hole. He paid out[2] the line for about a hundred feet and then stopped. The light was only a feeble glimmer down below and revealed nothing. Calvin lowered the light another hundred feet and this time it was only a twinkling speck as it swung at the end of the line. Calvin released another long length of twine and another and another and now the light was no longer visible, and the large ball of twine had shrunk to a small tangle.

"Almost a full thousand feet," he whispered in awe. "And no bottom yet. Might as well pull it up."

But the line did not come up with Calvin's pull. It stretched and grew taut, but it did not yield to his tugging.

"Must be caught on something," Calvin muttered, and gave the line a sharp jerk. In response there was a downward jerk that almost tore the line from his hands.

"Hey," yelled Calvin. "The line . . . it jerked!"

"But, Calvin," Dora protested.

"Don't Calvin me. I tell you there's something on the end of this line."

He gave another tug, and again the line was almost pulled from his hands. He tied the line to the stake and sat down to ponder the matter.

"It don't make sense," he said, more to himself than to Dora. "What could be down underground a good thousand feet?"

Tentatively he reached over and pulled lightly on the line. This time there was no response, and rapidly he began hauling it up. When the end of the line came into view, there was no flashlight attached to it. Instead, there was a small white pouch of a leatherlike substance.

Calvin opened the pouch with trembling fingers and shook into his palm a bar of yellow metal and a folded piece of parchment. The bar of metal was not large but seemed heavy for its size. Calvin got out his jackknife and scratched the point of the blade across the metal. The knife blade bit into it easily.

2 **paid out:** released

"Gold," said Calvin, his voice shaky. "Must be a whole pound of it . . . and just for a measly flashlight. They must be crazy down there."

He thrust the gold bar into his pocket and opened the small piece of parchment. One side was closely covered with a fine script. Calvin turned it this way and that and then tossed it on the ground.

"Foreigners," he said. "No wonder they ain't got any sense. But it's plain they need flashlights."

"But, Calvin," said Dora. "How could they get *down* there? There ain't any mines in this part of the country."

"Ain't you ever heard of them secret government projects?" asked Calvin scornfully. "This must be one of them. Now I'm going to town and get me a load of flashlights. They must need them bad. Now, mind you watch that hole good. Don't let no one go near it!"

Calvin strode to the battered pick-up which was standing near the barn, and a minute later was rattling down the highway towards Harmony Junction.

Dora picked up the bit of parchment which Calvin had thrown away. She could make nothing of the writing on it. It was all very strange. If it were some secret government undertaking, why would foreigners be engaged in it? And why would they need flashlights so urgently as to pay a fortune for one?

Suddenly it occurred to her that possibly the people down below didn't know there were English-speaking people up above. She hurried into the house and rummaged through Calvin's rickety desk for paper and pencil. In her search she found a small, ragged dictionary, and she took this with her to the kitchen table. Spelling did not come easy to Dora.

Her note was a series of questions. Why were they down there? Who were they? Why did they pay so much for an old flashlight?

As she started for the well it occurred to her that possibly the people down there might be hungry. She went back to the kitchen and wrapped a loaf of bread and a fair-sized piece of ham in a clean dish towel. She added a postscript to her note apologizing for the fact that she had nothing better to offer them. Then the thought came to her that since the people down below were obviously foreigners and possibly not too well versed in English, the small dictionary might be of help to them in answering her note. She wrapped the dictionary with the food in the towel.

It took Dora a long while to lower the bucket, but finally the twine grew slack in her hands, and she knew the bucket had reached the bottom. She waited a few moments and then tugged the line gently. The line held firm below, and Dora seated herself on the pile of soil to wait.

The warm sunlight felt good on her back, and it was pleasant to sit and do nothing. She had no fear that Calvin would return soon. She knew that nothing on earth—or under it—could keep Calvin from visiting a number of taverns once he was in town, and that with each tavern visited time would become more and more meaningless to him. She doubted that he would return before morning.

After a half hour Dora gave the line a questioning tug, but it did not yield. She did not mind. It was seldom that she had time to idle away. Usually when Calvin went to town, he burdened her with chores to be done during his absence, coupling each order with a threat of what awaited her should his instructions not be carried out.

Dora waited another half hour before giving the line another tug. This time there was a sharp answering jerk, and Dora began hauling the bucket upward. It seemed much heavier now, and twice she had to pause for a rest. When the bucket reached the surface, she saw why it was heavier.

"My goodness," she murmured as she viewed the dozen or so yellow metal bars in the bucket. "They must be real hungry down there!"

A sheet of the strange parchment was also in the bucket, and Dora picked it out expecting to see the strange script of the first note.

"Well, I declare," she said when she saw that the note was in English. It was in the same print as the dictionary, and each letter had been made with meticulous care.

She read the note slowly, shaping each word with her lips as she read.

Your language is barbaric, but the crude code book you sent down made it easy for our scholars to decipher it. We, too, wonder about you. How have you overcome the problem of living in the deadly light? Our legends tell of a race living on the surface, but intelligent reasoning has forced us to ridicule these old tales until now. We would still doubt that you are surface dwellers except for the fact that our instruments show without question that the opening above us leads to the deadly light.

The clumsy death ray which you sent us indicates that your scientific development is very low. Other than an artifact of another race it has no value to us. We sent gold as a courtesy payment only.

The food you call bread is not acceptable to our digestive systems, but the ham is beyond price. It is obviously the flesh of some creature, and we will exchange a double weight of gold for all that you can send us. Send more immediately. Also send a concise history of your race and arrange for your best scientists, such as they are, to communicate with us.

Glar, the Master

"Land sakes," said Dora. "Real bossy they are. I've a good mind not to send them *anything*. I don't dast[3] send them more ham. Calvin would notice if any more is gone."

Dora took the gold bars to her petunia bed beside the house and buried them in the loose black soil. She paid no heed to the sound of a car coming down the highway at high speed until it passed the house and wild squawking sounded above the roar of the motor. She hurried around to the front of the house, knowing already what had happened. She stared in dismay at the four white leghorns[4] which lay along the road. Now Calvin would charge her with negligence and beat her into unconsciousness.

Fear sharpened her wits. Perhaps if she could dispose of the bodies Calvin would think foxes had got them. Hastily she gathered up the dead chickens and feathers which lay scattered about. When she was finished, there was no evidence of the disaster.

She carried the chickens to the back of the house wondering how she could best dispose of them. Suddenly, as she glanced toward the hole, the answer came to her.

An hour later the four chickens were dressed and neatly cut up. Ignoring the other instructions in the note, she sent the bulky parcel of chicken down into the hole.

She sat down again to enjoy the luxury of doing nothing. When, an hour later, she picked up the line, there was an immediate response from below. The bucket was exceedingly heavy this time, and she was fearful

3 **dast:** dare
4 **leghorns:** a breed of small, hardy chickens

that the line might break. She was dizzy with fatigue when she finally hauled the bucket over to the edge of the hole. This time there were several dozen bars of gold in it and a brief note in the same precise lettering as before.

Our scientists are of the opinion that the flesh you sent down is that of a creature you call chicken. This is the supreme food. Never have we eaten anything so delicious. To show our appreciation we are sending you a bonus payment. Your code book indicates that there is a larger creature similar to chicken called turkey. Send us turkey immediately. I repeat, send us turkey immediately.

Glar, the Master

"Land sakes," gasped Dora. "They must have et that chicken raw. Now where in tarnation would I get a turkey?"

She buried the gold bars in another part of her petunia bed.

Calvin returned about ten o'clock the next morning. His eyes were bloodshot, and his face was a mottled red. The loose skin on his neck hung lower than usual and more than ever he reminded Dora of something which eluded her.

Calvin stepped down from the pick-up, and Dora cringed, but he seemed too tired and preoccupied to bother with her. He surveyed the hole glumly, then got back into the truck and backed it to the edge of the mound of earth. On the back of the truck was a winch[5] with a large drum of steel cable.

"Fix me something to eat," he ordered Dora.

Dora hurried into the house and began preparing ham and eggs. Each moment she expected Calvin to come in and demand to know, with a few blows, what was holding up his meal. But Calvin seemed very busy in the vicinity of the hole. When Dora went out to call him to eat, she found he had done a surprising amount of work. He had attached an oil drum to the steel cable. This hung over a heavy steel rod which rested across the hole. Stakes driven into the ground on each side of the hole held the rod in place.

"Your breakfast is ready, Calvin," said Dora.

"Shut up," Calvin answered.

5 **winch**: a piece of machinery used to lift heavy objects

The winch was driven by an electric motor, and Calvin ran a cable from the motor to an electric outlet on the yard lightpost.

From the cab he took a number of boxes and placed them in the oil drum.

"A whole hundred of them," he chuckled, more to himself than to Dora. "Fifty-nine cents apiece. Peanuts . . . one bar of gold will buy thousands."

Calvin threw the switch which controlled the winch, and with sickening force Dora suddenly realized the terrible thing that would soon happen. The creatures down below had no use or regard for flashlights.

Down went the oil drum, the cable screeching shrilly as it passed over the rod above the hole. Calvin got an oil can from the truck and applied oil generously to the rod and cable.

In a very short while the cable went slack and Calvin stopped the winch.

"I'll give them an hour to load up the gold," he said and went to the kitchen for his delayed breakfast.

Dora was practically in a state of shock. What would happen when the flashlights came back up with an insulting note in English was too horrible to contemplate. Calvin would learn about the gold she had received and very likely kill her.

Calvin ate his breakfast leisurely. Dora busied herself with household tasks, trying with all her might to cast out of her mind the terrible thing which was soon to happen.

Finally Calvin glanced at the wall clock, yawned widely, and tapped out his pipe. Ignoring Dora he went out to the hole. In spite of her terrible fear Dora could not resist following him. It was as if some power outside herself forced her to go.

The winch was already reeling[6] in the cable when she got to the hole. It seemed only seconds before the oil drum was up. The grin on Calvin's face was broad as he reached out over the hole and dragged the oil drum to the edge. A look of utter disbelief replaced the grin as he looked into the drum. His Adam's apple seemed to vibrate, and once again part of Dora's mind tried to recall what it was that Calvin reminded her of.

Calvin was making flat, bawling sounds like a lost calf. He hauled the drum out of the hole and dumped its contents on the ground. The flashlights, many of them dented and with lenses broken, made a sizeable pile.

6 **reeling:** pulling

With a tremendous kick Calvin sent flashlights flying in all directions. One, with a note attached, landed at Dora's feet. Either Calvin was so blinded by rage that he didn't see it, or he assumed it was written in the same unreadable script as the first note.

"You down there," he screamed into the hole. "You filthy swine. I'll fix you. I'll make you sorry you ever double-crossed me. I'll . . . I'll . . ."

He dashed for the house, and Dora hastily snatched up the note.

You are even more stupid than we thought [she read]. *Your clumsy death rays are useless to us. We informed you of this. We want turkey. Send us turkey immediately.*

Glar, the Master

She crumpled the note swiftly as Calvin came from the house with his double-barrelled shotgun. For a moment Dora thought that he knew everything and was about to kill her.

"Please, Calvin," she said.

"Shut up," Calvin said. "You saw me work the winch. Can you do it?"

"Why, yes, but what. . .?"

"Listen, you stupid cow. I'm going down there and fix those dirty foreigners. You send me down and bring me up." He seized Dora by the shoulder. "And if you mess things, I'll fix you, too! I'll really and truly fix you."

Dora nodded dumbly.

Calvin put his gun in the oil drum and pushed it to the centre of the hole. Then, hanging on to the cable, he carefully lowered himself into the drum.

"Give me just one hour to run those dirty rats down, then bring me back up," he said.

Dora threw the switch and the oil drum went down. When the cable slackened, she stopped the winch. She spent most of the hour praying that Calvin would not find the people down below and become a murderer.

Exactly an hour later Dora started the oil drum upward. The motor laboured mightily as though under a tremendous strain, and the cable seemed stretched almost to the breaking point.

Dora gasped when the oil drum came into view. Calvin was not in it! She shut off the motor and hastened to the drum, half expecting to find Calvin crouching down inside. But Calvin was not there. Instead there were scores of gold bars and on top of them a sheet of the familiar white parchment.

"Land sakes," Dora said, as she took in a full view of the drum's contents. She had no idea of the value of the treasure upon which she gazed. She only knew it must be immense. Carefully, she reached down and picked out the note, which she read in her slow, precise manner:

Not even the exquisite flavour of the chicken compares to the incomparable goodness of the live turkey you sent down to us. We must confess that our concept of turkey was quite different, but this is of no consequence. So delectable was the turkey that we are again sending you a bonus payment. We implore you to send us more turkey immediately.

Glar, the Master

Dora read the note a second time to make sure she understood it fully. "Well, I declare," she said in considerable wonder. "I declare." ༺

Pet Haiku

DOGS

I love my master;
Thus I perfume myself with
This long-rotten squirrel.

I lie belly-up
In the sunshine, happier than
You ever will be.

I sound the alarm!
Paperboy—come to kill us all—
Look! Look! Look! Look! Look!

I sound the alarm!
Garbage man—come to kill us all—
Look! Look! Look! Look! Look!

How do I love thee?
The ways are numberless as
My hairs on the rug.

My human is home!
I am so ecstatic I have
Made a puddle.

I hate my choke chain—
Look, world, they strangle me! Ack
Ack Ack Ack Ack Ack!

Sleeping here, my chin
On your foot—no greater bliss—well,
Maybe catching rats.

Look in my eyes and
Deny it. No human could
Love you as much as I do.

I am your best friend,
Now, always, and especially
When you are eating.

Dig under fence—why?
Because it's there. Because it's
There. Because it's there.

CATS

NANCEE BELSHAW

You never feed me.
Perhaps I'll sleep on your face.
That will show you.

Small brave carnivores
Kill pine cones and mosquitoes;
Fear vacuum cleaner.

The rule for today,
Touch my tail, I shred your hand.
New rule tomorrow.

Want to trim my claws?
Don't even think about it!
My yelps will wake the dead.

Grace personified
I leap into the window.
I meant to do that.

I want to be close
To you. Can I fit my head
inside your armpit?

The mighty hunter
Returns with gifts of plump birds.
Your foot just squashed one.

Wanna go outside.
Oh, no! Help! I got outside!
Let me back inside!

You're always typing.
Well, let's see you ignore my
Sitting on your hands.

Humans are so strange.
Mine lies still in the bed, then screams!
My claws aren't that sharp . . .

Terrible battle!
I fought for hours. Come and see!
What's a "term paper?"

A Conversation with My Dogs

MERRILL MARKOE

It is late afternoon. Seated at my desk, I call for my dogs to join me in my office. They do.

ME. The reason I've summoned you here today is I really think we should talk about something.

BOB. What's that?

ME. Well, please don't take this the wrong way, but I get the feeling you guys think you *have* to follow me *everywhere* and I just want you both to know that you don't.

STAN. Where would you get a feeling like that?

ME. I get it from the fact that the both of you follow me *everywhere* all day long. Like for instance, this morning. We were all together in the bedroom? Why do you both look blank? Doesn't this ring a bell at all? I was on the bed reading the paper . . .

BOB. Where was I?

ME. On the floor sleeping.

BOB. On the floor sleepi . . . ? Oh, yes. Right, I remember that. Go on.

ME. So, there came a point where I had to get up and go into the next room to get a Kleenex. And you *both* woke up out of a deep sleep to go with me.

STAN. Yes. So? What's the problem?

BOB. We *like* to watch you get Kleenex. We happen to think it's something you do very well.

ME. The point I'm trying to make is why do you both have to get up out of a deep sleep to go *with* me. You sit there staring at me, all excited, like you think something really good is going to happen. I feel a lot of pressure to be more entertaining.

BOB. Would it help if we stood?

STAN. I think what the lady is saying is that where Kleenex retrieval is concerned, she'd just as soon we not make the trip.

BOB. Is that true?

ME. Yes. It is.

BOB. *(deeply hurt):* Oh, man.

STAN. Don't let her get to you, buddy.

BOB. I know I shouldn't. But it all comes as such a shock.

ME. I think you may be taking this wrong. It's not that I don't like your company. It's just that I see no reason for you both to follow me every time I get up.

BOB. What if just one of us goes?

STAN. And I don't suppose that "one of us" would be *you?*

ME. *Neither* of you needs to go.

BOB. Okay. Fine. No problem. Get your damn Kleenex alone from now on.

ME. Good.

BOB. I'm just curious. What's your position on pens?

ME. Pens?

BOB. Yes. How many of us can wake up out of a deep sleep to watch you look for a pen?

ME. Why would *either* of you want to wake up out of a deep sleep to follow me around while I'm looking for a pen?

STAN. Is she serious?

BOB. I can't tell. She has such a weird sense of humor.

ME. Let's just level with each other, okay? The *real* reason you both follow me every place I go is that you secretly believe there might be food involved. Isn't that true? Isn't that the real reason for the show of enthusiasm?

STAN. Very nice talk.

BOB. The woman has got some mouth on her.

ME. You mean you *deny* that every time you follow me out of the room it's actually because you think we're stopping for snacks?

BOB. Absolutely false. That is a bald-faced lie. We do it for the life experience. Period.

STAN. And sometimes I think it might work into a game of ball.

BOB. But we certainly don't *expect* anything.

STAN. We're *way* past expecting anything of you. We wouldn't want you to overexert yourself in any way. You have to rest and save up all your strength for all that Kleenex fetching.

BOB. Plus we know it doesn't concern you in the least that we're both *starving to death.*

STAN. We consume on the average about a third of the calories eaten daily by the typical wasted South American street dog.

ME. *One* bowl of food a day is what the *vet* said I should give you. No more.

BOB. One bowl of food is a joke. It's an hors d'oeuvre.[1] It does nothing but whet my appetite.

ME. Last summer, before I cut your food down, you were the size and shape of a hassock.[2]

BOB. Who is she talking to?

STAN. You, pal. You looked like a beanbag chair, buddy.

BOB. But it was not from overeating. In summer, I retain fluids, that's all. I was in very good shape.

STAN. For a hippo. I saw you play ball back then. Nice energy. For a dead guy.

BOB. Don't talk to me about energy. Who singlehandedly ate his way through the back fence. Not just once but on *four separate occasions?*

ME. So *you're* the one who did that?

BOB. One who did what?

ME. Ate through the back fence.

BOB. Is there something wrong with the back fence? I have no idea what happened. Whoever said that is a liar.

1 **hors d'oeuvre:** tidbit of food; appetizer
2 **hassock:** a low stool

STAN. The fact remains that we are starving all day long and you continually torture us by eating right in front of us.

BOB. Very nice manners, by the way.

ME. You have the nerve to discuss my manners? Who drinks out of the toilet and then comes up and kisses me on the face?

BOB. That would be Stan.

ME. No. That would be *you*. And while we're on the subject of manners, who keeps trying to crawl *into* the refrigerator? Who always has *mud* on their tongue?

STAN. Well, that would be Bob.

ME. Okay. That *would* be Bob. But the point I'm trying to make is that where manners are concerned, let's just say that you don't catch me trying to stick my head in *your* dinner.

BOB. Well, that may be more a function of menu than anything else.

ME. Which brings me right back to my original point. The two of you do not have to wake up and offer me fake camaraderie[3] now that you understand that *once* a day is all you're ever going to be fed. Period. Nonnegotiable. For the rest of your natural lives. And if I want to play ball, I'll *say* so. End of sentence.

STAN. Well, I see that the nature of these talks has completely broken down.

BOB. I gotta tell you, it hurts.

ME. There's no reason to have hurt feelings.

STAN. Fine. Whatever you say.

BOB. I just don't care anymore. I'm beyond that, quite frankly. Get your own Kleenex, for all I care.

STAN. I feel the same way. Let her go get all the Kleenex and pens she wants. I couldn't care less.

ME. Excellent. Well, I hope we understand each other now.

BOB. We do. Why'd you get up? Where are you going?

ME. Into the next room.

STAN. Oh. Mm hmm. I see. And why is that?

ME. To get my purse.

---

3 **camaraderie:** companionship

STAN. Hey, fatso, out of my way.

BOB. Watch out. I was first.

STAN. *I* was first.

BOB. We're getting her purse, I go first. *I'm starving.*

STAN. You don't listen at all, do you. Going for *pens* means food. She said she's getting her *purse*. That means ball. ◕

Responding to Cluster Three

What Are Some Types of Humor?
Thinking Skill CLASSIFYING

1. Among the concept vocabulary terms on page 13 are various types of humor. These include jokes, slapstick, farce, black humor, parody, puns, stand-up comedy, satire, and more. Using these terms and a chart such as the one below, label the selections from this cluster. Then choose five other selections from previous clusters to list and **classify**. Some selections, such as "Money: Too Tight to Mention," which has elements of both satire and stand-up comedy, may overlap. You may give such selections more than one classification.

Selection	Type(s) of Humor
The Clown	
Word Wit	
Hey, You Down There	
Pet Haiku	
A Conversation with My Dogs	

2. **Foreshadowing** is a technique authors use to hint at what is going to happen later in a piece. In "Hey, You Down There" when did you realize what Calvin reminded Dora of? Did you see the ending coming, and if so, did guessing what was going to happen heighten or diminish your enjoyment of the story?

3. Continue using the Laugh-O-Meter chart you filled out for Clusters One and Two to rank the humor quotient of the selections in this cluster.

4. You have sampled many types of humor in this book. Which two appeal to you most? Explain your answer.

Writing Activity: Pick up the humor pen
Now that you have read and analyzed several clusters of humor, it is your turn. Pick a topic. Then using a humor format such as hyperbole, slapstick, or parody, try your hand at writing something funny.

To Write a Humor Piece
- select a topic
- choose a humor format
- write a rough draft
- read it aloud
- have a friend, classmate, or family member read it and make suggestions for improvement
- revise and polish it
- if your teacher directs, perform or read your work to the class

CLUSTER FOUR

Thinking on Your Own
Thinking Skill SYNTHESIZING

HEE HEE
HEE HEE

HA HA
HA HA

Light Verse

Spill Check Pome

Eye halve a spelling checker
It came with my pea sea
It plainly marquees four my revue
Miss steaks eye kin knot sea.

Eye strike a key and type a word
And weight four it two say
Weather eye am wrong oar write
It shows me strait a weigh.

As soon as a mist ache is maid
It nose bee fore two long
And eye can put the error rite
Its rare lea ever wrong.

Eye have run this poem threw it
I am shore your pleased two no
Its letter perfect awl the weigh
My checker tolled me sew.

—SORES UNKNOWN

Limericks

BY COSMO MONKHOUSE

There was a young lady of Niger
Who smiled as she rode on a tiger.
    They returned from the ride
    With the lady inside,
And the smile on the face of the tiger.

BY CAROLYN WELLS

A tutor who tooted the flute
Tried to tutor two tooters to toot.
    Said the two to the tutor,
    "Is it harder to toot or
To tutor two tooters to toot?"

ANONYMOUS

There was an old man of Blackheath
Who sat on his set of false teeth.
    Said he with a start,
    "O Lord, bless my heart!
I've bitten myself underneath!"

Shotgun Cheatham's
Last Night Above Ground

RICHARD PECK

The first time I ever saw a dead body, it was Shotgun Cheatham. We were staying with our Grandma Dowdel, and it was the best trip by far we ever made to her house. My sister Mary Alice and I visited at Grandma Dowdel's every summer when our folks went up to fish in Wisconsin on Dad's week off.

"They dump us on her is what they do," Mary Alice said. She'd have been about nine the year they buried Shotgun. She didn't like going to Grandma's because you had to go outside to the privy.[1] A big old snaggle-toothed tomcat lived in the cobhouse,[2] and as quick as you'd come out of the privy, he'd jump at you. Mary Alice hated that.

I liked going to Grandma's because we went on the train. You could go just about anywhere on a train in those days, and I didn't care where a train went as long as I was on it. The tracks cut through the town where Grandma Dowdel lived, and people stood out on their porches to see the train go through. It was a town that size.

Mary Alice said there was nothing to do and nobody to do it with, so she'd tag after me, though I was three years older and a boy. We'd stroll uptown, which was three brick buildings: the bank, the general merchandise, and The Coffee Pot Cafe where the old saloon had stood. Prohibition[3] was on in those days, so people made beer at home. They

---

1 **privy:** outdoor toilet

2 **cobhouse:** a structure where corncobs are stored

3 **Prohibition:** laws against the making and sale of alcohol

still had the tin roofs out over the sidewalk and hitching rails. Most farmers came to town horse-drawn, though there were Fords, and the banker drove a Hupmobile.[4]

But it was a slow place except for the time they buried Shotgun Cheatham. He might have made it unnoticed all the way to the grave except for his name. The county seat newspaper didn't want to run an obituary on anybody called Shotgun, but nobody knew any other name for him. This sparked attention from some of the bigger newspapers. One sent in a stringer[5] to nose around The Coffee Pot Cafe for a human-interest story since it was August, a slow month for news.

The Coffee Pot was where people went to loaf, talk tall, and swap gossip. Mary Alice and I were regulars there, and even we were of some interest because we were kin of Mrs. Dowdel's who never set foot in the place. She kept herself to herself, which was uphill work in a town like that.

Mary Alice and I carried the tale home that a suspicious type had come off the train in citified clothes and a stiff straw hat. He stuck out a mile and was asking around about Shotgun Cheatham. And he was taking notes.

4 **Hupmobile:** a long touring car with bucket seats

5 **stringer:** part-time reporter

125

Grandma had already heard it on the grapevine that Shotgun was no more, though she wasn't the first person people ran to with news. She wasn't what you'd call a popular woman. Grandpa Dowdel had been well thought of, but he was long gone.

That day she was working tomatoes on the black iron range, and her kitchen was hot enough to steam the calendars off the wall. Her sleeves were turned back, and she had arms on her like a man. When she heard the town was apt to fill up with newspaper reporters, her jaw clenched.

Presently she said, "I'll tell you what that reporter's after. He wants to get the horselaugh on us because he thinks we're nothing but a bunch of hayseeds and no-'count country people. We are, but what business is it of his?"

"Who was Shotgun Cheatham anyway?" Mary Alice asked.

"He was just an old reprobate[6] who lived poor and died broke," Grandma said. "Nobody went near him because he smelled like a polecat. He lived in a chicken coop, and now they'll have to burn it down."

To change the subject she said to me, "Here, you stir these tomatoes, and don't let them stick. I've stood in this heat till I'm half-cooked myself."

I hated it when Grandma gave me kitchen work. I wished it was her day for apple butter. She made that outdoors over an open fire, and she put pennies in the caldron to keep it from sticking.

"Down at The Coffee Pot they say Shotgun rode with the James boys."

"Which James boys?" Grandma asked.

"Jesse James," I said, "and Frank."

"They wouldn't have had him," she said. "Anyhow, those Jameses were Missouri people."

"They were telling the reporter Shotgun killed a man and went to the penitentiary."[7]

"Several around here done that," Grandma said, "though I don't recall him being out of town any length of time. Who's doing all this talking?"

"A real old, humped-over lady with buck teeth," Mary Alice said.

"Cross-eyed?" Grandma said. "That'd be Effie Wilcox. You think she's ugly now, you should have seen her as a girl. And she'd talk you to death. Her tongue's attached in the middle and flaps at both ends." Grandma was over by the screen door for a breath of air.

6 **reprobate:** an unworthy person
7 **penitentiary:** prison

"They said he'd notched his gun in six places," I said, pushing my luck. "They said the notches were either for banks he'd robbed or for sheriffs he'd shot."

"Was that Effie again? Never trust an ugly woman. She's got a grudge against the world," said Grandma, who was no oil painting herself. She fetched up a sigh. "I'll tell you how Shotgun got his name. He wasn't but about ten years old, and he wanted to go out and shoot quail with a bunch of older boys. He couldn't hit a barn wall from the inside, and he had a sty[8] in one eye. They were out there in a pasture without a quail in sight, but Shotgun got all excited being with the big boys. He squeezed off a round and killed a cow. Down she went. If he'd been aiming at her, she'd have died of old age eventually. The boys took the gun off him, not knowing who he'd plug next. That's how he got the name, and it stuck to him like flypaper. Any girl in town could have outshot him, and that includes me." Grandma jerked a thumb at herself.

She kept a twelve-gauge double-barreled Winchester Model 21 behind the woodbox, but we figured it had been Grandpa Dowdel's for shooting ducks. "And I wasn't no Annie Oakley myself, except with squirrels." Grandma was still at the door, fanning her apron. Then in the same voice she said, "Looks like we got company. Take them tomatoes off the fire."

A stranger was on the porch, and when Mary Alice and I crowded up behind Grandma to see, it was the reporter. He was sharp-faced, and he'd sweated through his hatband.

"What's your business?" Grandma said through screen wire, which was as friendly as she got.

"Ma'am, I'm making inquiries about the late Shotgun Cheatham." He shuffled his feet, wanting to get one of them in the door. Then he mopped up under his hat brim with a silk handkerchief. His Masonic ring had diamond chips in it.

"Who sent you to me?"

"I'm going door-to-door, ma'am. You know how you ladies like to talk. Bless your hearts, you'd all talk the hind leg off a mule."

Mary Alice and I both stared at that. We figured Grandma would grab up her broom to swat him off the porch. She could make short work of peddlers even when they weren't lippy. And tramps never marked her

---

8 **sty:** an inflamed swelling at the inside edge of the eyelid

fence.[9] But to our surprise she swept open the screen door and stepped out on the back porch. You didn't get inside her house even if you knew her. I followed and so did Mary Alice once she was sure the snaggle-toothed tom wasn't lurking around out there, waiting to pounce.

"You a newspaper reporter?" she said. "Peoria?" It was the flashy clothes, but he looked surprised. "What they been telling you?"

"Looks like I got a good story by the tail," he said. "'Last of the Old Owlhoot Gunslingers Goes to a Pauper's Grave.' That kind of angle. Ma'am, I wonder if you could help me flesh out the story some."

"Well, I got flesh to spare," Grandma said mildly. "Who's been talking to you?"

"It was mainly an elderly lady—"

"Ugly as sin, calls herself Wilcox?" Grandma said. "She's been in the state hospital for the insane until just here lately, but as a reporter I guess you nosed that out."

Mary Alice nudged me hard, and the reporter's eyes widened.

"They tell you how Shotgun come by his name?"

"Opinions seem to vary, ma'am."

"Ah well, fame is fleeting," Grandma said. "He got it in the Civil War."

The reporter's hand hovered over his breast pocket where a notepad stuck out.

"Oh yes, Shotgun went right though the war with the Illinois Volunteers. Shiloh in the spring of sixty-two, and he was with U. S. Grant when Vicksburg fell. That's where he got his name. Grant give it to him, in fact. Shotgun didn't hold with government-issue firearms. He shot rebels with his old Remington pump-action that he'd used to kill quail back here at home."

Now Mary Alice was yanking on my shirttail. We knew kids lie all the time, but Grandma was no kid, and she could tell some whoppers. Of course the reporter had been lied to big-time up at the cafe, but Grandma's lies were more interesting, even historical. They made Shotgun look better while they left Effie Wilcox in the dust.

"He was always a crack shot," she said, winding down. "Come home from the war with a line of medals bigger than his chest."

"And yet he died penniless," the reporter said in a thoughtful voice.

---

9 **marked her fence:** during the Depression, tramps and hoboes used to mark fences of homes to alert other wanderers of what to expect

"Oh well, he'd sold off them medals and give the money to war widows and orphans."

A change crossed the reporter's narrow face. Shotgun had gone from kill-crazy gunslinger to war hero marksman. Philanthropist,[10] even. He fumbled his notepad out and was scribbling. He thought he'd hit pay dirt with Grandma. "It's all a matter of record," she said. "You could look it up."

He was ready to wire in a new story: "Civil War Hero Handpicked by U. S. Grant called to the Great Campground in the Sky." Something like that. "And he never married?"

"Never did," Grandma said. "He broke Effie Wilcox's heart. She's bitter still, as you see."

"And now he goes to a pauper's grave with none to mark his passing," the reporter said, which may have been a sample of his writing style.

"They tell you that?" Grandma said. "They're pulling your leg, sonny. You drop by The Coffee Pot and tell them you heard that Shotgun's being buried from my house with full honors. He'll spend his last night above ground in my front room, and you're invited."

The reporter backed down the porch stairs, staggering under all this new material. "Much obliged, ma'am," he said.

"Happy to help," Grandma said.

Mary Alice had turned loose of my shirttail. What little we knew about grown-ups never seemed to cover Grandma. She turned on us. "Now I've got to change my shoes and walk all the way up to the lumberyard in this heat," she said, as if she hadn't brought it all on herself. Up at the lumberyard they'd be knocking together Shotgun Cheatham's coffin and sending the bill to the county, and Grandma had to tell them to bring that coffin to her house, with Shotgun in it.

▲ ▲ ▲

By nightfall a green pine coffin stood on two sawhorses in the bay window of the front room, and people milled in the yard. They couldn't see Shotgun from there because the coffin lid blocked the view. Besides, a heavy gauze hung from the open lid and down over the front of the coffin to veil him. Shotgun hadn't been exactly fresh when they discovered his body. Grandma had flung open every window, but there was a peculiar smell in the room. I'd only had one look at him when they'd carried in the coffin, and that was enough. I'll tell you just two things about him. He didn't have his teeth in, and he was wearing bib overalls.

10 **philanthropist:** one who helps and/or gives money to those in need

The people in the yard still couldn't believe Grandma was holding open house. This didn't stop the reporter who was haunting the parlor, looking for more flesh to add to his story. And it didn't stop Mrs. L. J. Weidenbach, the banker's wife, who came leading her father, an ancient codger[11] half her size in full Civil War Union blue.

"We are here to pay our respects at this sad time," Mrs. Weidenbach said when Grandma let them in. "When I told Daddy that Shotgun had been decorated by U. S. Grant and wounded three times at Bull Run, it brought it all back to him, and we had to come." Her old daddy wore a forage cap[12] and a decoration from the Grand Army of the Republic, and he seemed to have no idea where he was. She led him up to the coffin, where they admired the flowers. Grandma had planted a pitcher of glads[13] from her garden at either end of the pine box. In each pitcher she'd stuck an American flag.

A few more people willing to brave Grandma came and went, but finally we were down to the reporter who'd settled into the best chair, still nosing for news. Then who appeared at the front door but Mrs. Effie Wilcox, in a hat.

"Mrs. Dowdel, I've come to set with you overnight and see our brave old soldier through his Last Watch."

In those days people sat up with a corpse through the final night before burial. I'd have bet money Grandma wouldn't let Mrs. Wilcox in for a quick look, let alone overnight. But of course Grandma was putting on the best show possible to pull wool over the reporter's eyes. Little though she thought of townspeople, she thought less of strangers. Grandma waved Mrs. Wilcox inside, and in she came, her eyes all over the place. She made for the coffin, stared at the blank white gauze, and said, "Don't he look natural?"

Then she drew up a chair next to the reporter. He flinched because he had it on good authority that she'd just been let out of an insane asylum. "Warm, ain't it?" she said straight at him, but looking everywhere.

The crowd outside finally dispersed. Mary Alice and I hung at the edge of the room, too curious to be anywhere else.

"If you're here for the long haul," Grandma said to the reporter, "how about a beer?" He looked encouraged, and Grandma left him to Mrs.

---

11 **codger:** a mildly eccentric fellow

12 **forage cap:** a small military cap with a visor and round, flat crown

13 **glads:** short form of gladiolas; a gladiola is a type of flower

Wilcox, which was meant as a punishment. She came back with three of her home brews, cellar-cool. She brewed beer to drink herself, but these three bottles were to see the reporter though the night. She wouldn't have expected her worse enemy, Effie Wilcox, to drink alcohol in front of a man.

In normal circumstances the family recalls stories about the departed to pass the long night hours. But these circumstances weren't normal, and quite a bit had already been recalled about Shotgun Cheatham anyway.

Only a single lamp burned, and as midnight drew on, the glads drooped in their pitchers. I was wedged in a corner, beginning to doze, and Mary Alice was sound asleep on a throw rug. After the second beer, the reporter lolled,[14] visions of Shotgun's Civil War glories no doubt dancing in his head. You could hear the tick of the kitchen clock. Grandma's chin would drop, then jerk back. Mrs. Wilcox had been humming "Rock of Ages," but tapered off after "let me hide myself in thee."

Then there was the quietest sound you ever heard. Somewhere between a rustle and a whisper. It brought me around, and I saw Grandma sit forward and cock her head. I blinked to make sure I was awake, and the whole world seemed to listen. Not a leaf trembled outside.

But the gauze that hung down over the open coffin moved. Twitched.

Except for Mary Alice, we all saw it. The reporter sat bolt upright, and Mrs. Wilcox made a little sound.

Then nothing.

Then the gauze rippled as if a hand had passed across it from the other side, and in one place it wrinkled into a wad as if somebody had snagged it. As if a feeble hand had reached up from the coffin depths in one last desperate attempt to live before the dirt was shoveled in.

Every hair on my head stood up.

"Naw," Mrs. Wilcox said, strangling. She pulled back in her chair, and her hat went forward. "Naw!"

The reporter had his chair arms in a death grip. "Sweet mother of—"

But Grandma rocketed out of her chair. "Whoa, Shotgun!" she bellowed. "You've had your time, boy. You don't get no more!"

She galloped out of the room faster than I'd ever seen her move. The reporter was riveted, and Mrs. Wilcox was sinking fast.

---

14 **lolled:** drooped

Quicker than it takes to tell, Grandma was back and already raised to her aproned shoulder was the twelve-gauge Winchester from behind the woodbox. She swung it wildly around the room, skimming Mrs. Wilcox's hat, and took aim at the gauze that draped the yawning coffin. Then she squeezed off a round.

I thought that sound would bring the house down. I couldn't hear right for a week. Then Grandma roared out, "Rest in peace, I tell you, you old—" Then she let fly with the other barrel.

The reporter came out of the chair and whipped completely around in a circle. Beer bottles went everywhere. The straight route to the front door was in Grandma's line of fire, and he didn't have the presence of mind to realize she'd already discharged both barrels. He went out a side window, headfirst, leaving his hat and his notepad behind. Which he feared more, the living dead or Grandma's aim, he didn't tarry to tell.

Mrs. Wilcox was on her feet, hollering, "The dead is walking, and Mrs. Dowdel's gunning for me!" She cut and ran out the door and into the night.

When the screen door snapped to behind her, silence fell. Mary Alice hadn't moved. The first explosion had blasted her awake, but she naturally thought that Grandma had killed her, so she didn't bother to budge. She says the whole experience gave her nightmares for years after.

A burned-powder haze hung in the room, cutting the smell of Shotgun Cheatham. The white gauze was black rags now, and Grandma had blown the lid clear off the coffin. She'd have blown out all three windows in the bay, except they were open. As it was, she'd pitted her woodwork bad and topped the snowball bushes outside. But apart from scattered shot,[15] she hadn't disfigured Shotgun Cheatham any more than he already was.

Grandma stood there savoring the silence. Then she turned toward the kitchen with the twelve-gauge loose in her hand. "Time you kids was in bed," she said as she trudged past us.

Apart from Grandma herself, I was the only one who'd seen her big old snaggle-toothed tomcat streak out of the coffin and over the windowsill when she let fire. And I supposed she'd seen him climb in, which gave her ideas. It was the cat, sitting smug on Shotgun Cheatham's breathless chest, who'd batted at the gauze the way a cat will. And he sure lit out the way he'd come when Grandma fired just over his ragged ears, as he'd probably used up eight lives already.

The cat in the coffin gave Grandma Dowdel her chance. She never had any time for Effie Wilcox, whose tongue flapped at both ends, but she had even less for newspaper reporters who think your business is theirs. Courtesy of the cat, she'd fired a round, so to speak, in the direction of each.

Though she never gloated, she looked satisfied. It certainly fleshed out her reputation and gave people new reason to leave her in peace. The story of Shotgun Cheatham's last night above ground kept The Coffee Pot Cafe fully engaged for the rest of that long summer. It was a story that grew in the telling in one of those little towns where there's always time to ponder all the different kinds of truth. ∞

---

15 **scatttered shot:** broadly scattered bits of buckshot

How to Eat Like a Child

Delia Ephron

PEAS: Mash and flatten into thin sheet on plate. Press the back of the fork into the peas. Hold fork vertically, prongs up, and lick off peas.

MASHED POTATOES: Pat mashed potatoes flat on top. Dig several little depressions. Think of them as ponds or pools. Fill the pools with gravy. With your fork, sculpt rivers between pools and watch the gravy flow between them. Decorate with peas. Do not eat.

Alternative method: Make a large hole in center of mashed potatoes. Pour in ketchup. Stir until potatoes turn pink. Eat as you would peas.

ANIMAL CRACKERS: Eat each in this order—legs, head, body.

SANDWICH: Leave the crusts. If your mother says you have to eat them because that's the best part, stuff the crusts into your pants pocket or between the cushions of the couch.

SPAGHETTI: Wind too many strands on the fork and make sure at least two strands dangle down. Open your mouth wide and stuff in spaghetti; suck noisily to inhale the dangling strands. Clean plate, ask for seconds, and eat only half. When carrying your plate to the kitchen, hold it tilted so that the remaining spaghetti slides off and onto the floor.

ICE-CREAM CONE: Ask for a double scoop. Knock the top scoop off while walking out the door of the ice-cream parlor. Cry. Lick the remaining scoop slowly so that ice cream melts down the outside of the cone and over your hand. Stop licking when the ice cream is even with the top of the cone. Be sure it is absolutely even. Eat a hole in the bottom of the cone and suck the rest of the ice cream out the bottom. When only the cone remains with ice cream coating the inside, leave on car dashboard.

ICE CREAM IN BOWL: Grip spoon upright in fist. Stir ice cream vigorously to make soup. Take a large helping on a spoon, place spoon in mouth, and slowly pull it out, sucking only the top layer of ice cream off. Wave spoon in air. Lick its back. Put in mouth again and suck off some more. Repeat until all ice cream is off spoon and begin again.

COOKED CARROTS: On way to mouth, drop in lap. Smuggle to garbage in napkin.

SPINACH: Divide into little piles. Rearrange into new piles. After five or six maneuvers, sit back and say you are full.

CHOCOLATE-CHIP COOKIES: Half-sit, half-lie on the bed, propped up by a pillow. Read a book. Place cookies next to you on the sheet so that crumbs get in the bed. As you eat the cookies, remove each chocolate chip and place it on your stomach. When all the cookies are consumed, eat the chips one by one, allowing two per page.

MILK SHAKE: Bite off one end of the paper covering the straw. Blow through straw to shoot paper across table. Place straw in shake and suck. When the shake just reaches your mouth, place a finger over the top of the straw—the pressure will keep the shake in the straw. Lift straw out of shake, put bottom end in mouth, release finger, and swallow.

Do this until the straw is squished so that you can't suck through it. Ask for another. Open it the same way, but this time shoot the paper at the waitress when she isn't looking. Sip your shake casually—you are just minding your own business—until there is about an inch of shake remaining. Then blow through the straw until bubbles rise to the top of the glass. When your father says he's had just about enough, get a stomachache.

CHEWING GUM: Remove from mouth and stretch into spaghetti-like strand. Swing like a lasso. Put back in mouth. Pulling out one end and gripping the other end between teeth, have your gum meet your friend's gum and press them together. Think that you have just done something really disgusting.

BAKED APPLE: With your fingers, peel skin off baked apple. Tell your mother you changed your mind, you don't want it. Later, when she is harassed and not paying attention to what she is doing, pick up the naked baked apple and hand it to her.

FRENCH FRIES: Wave one French fry in air for emphasis while you talk. Pretend to conduct orchestra. Then place four fries in your mouth at once and chew. Turn to your sister, open your mouth, and stick out your tongue coated with potatoes. Close mouth and swallow. Smile. ∾

A Houseful of
Love and Laughter

JAY LENO

Biologically speaking, I came late to the party. When I was born, my mother was 41, my dad was 42 and my brother was already ten. This built-in generation gap probably defined me every bit as much as my distinctly peculiar blood mix.

My mother, Catherine, was born in Scotland. My father, Angelo, was a first-generation Italian-American. I seem to be divided right down the middle. My Scottish side is practical, analytical, even a bit frugal.[1] My Italian side is loud, outgoing, ready to laugh (and be laughed at).

As an immigrant, my mother lived in constant fear of deportation. You could miss up to four questions on the citizenship test, and Mom missed five. The question she flunked on was: "What is the Constitution of the United States?" The answer she gave was: "A boat."

Which wasn't entirely wrong. The *USS Constitution* was docked in Boston. But the judge instantly denied her citizenship.

My father stormed up to the judge. "What the hell is this? Let me see the test! She's not wrong—the *Constitution* is a boat!"

The judge rolled his eyes and said, "No, the Constitution is our basic governing—"

"It's also a boat in Boston! The *Constitution!* Same thing! Come on!"

The judge finally couldn't take any more. He said, "Fine. She's a *citizen.* Now get out of here!"

So my father said to my mom, "You passed!"

1 **frugal:** thrifty

"No, I didn't pass," she whimpered. "They're going to come after me!" From then on, any time my mother was even in the proximity of a policeman, she quaked with fear. When I took her to Scotland in 1983, she asked me, "Will I be able to get back in?"

"Ma! Don't worry! That was 50 years ago! They don't know that you said *a boat*!" It never ended.

My First Fish Story.

My father always tried to get me to do outdoorsy things. He'd say, "Why don't you go fishing?" Fishing, to me, was like a nap with a stick.

"Just go," my mother told me. "If you catch one fish, you can at least show your father that you tried."

One day at school I heard they were draining a lake near our house and there were all these fish flopping around. So I rode my bike over and scooped up about 25.

I walked in the house and said, "Hey, Pop! Look what I caught!"

My father just beamed with pride. "Hey! Look at my boy! Look at all the fish he got there!"

Mom cut them open and started gagging. "These fish stink!" she said. "We can't eat them!"

"Oh, I'm sure they're fine!" Dad said. "What a little fisherman!"

My mother finally took me aside, and I confessed under threat of frying pan: "Okay, okay—I found 'em! They were all dead!" Mom was exasperated, but so as not to disappoint my dad, she ran out to the store and bought fresh fish, which she served that night. Dad never found out.

The Tape Is Rolling.

When I was in high school, my brother Pat was drafted into the Army and sent to Vietnam. Nobody in the family was much of a letter writer, so my father had the idea to get a miniature tape recorder to make voice messages.

The clerk at the electronics store asked, "How long a tape do you want—15 minutes?"

"*Fifteen minutes!*" Dad said. "We couldn't even say hello in 15 minutes! What's your *longest* tape?"

"Ninety minutes."

"That's more like it! Give me four!"

At home my father set up everything on the kitchen table and announced, "Okay, now we're all gonna talk to Pat!" He pressed the record button and in his own inimitable[2] way began: "HELLO, PAT! EVERYTHING HERE IS GOOD! I'M FINE! YOUR MOTHER'S FINE! HERE'S YOUR BROTHER! JAMIE, TALK TO PAT!"

I stepped forward: "Hey, Pat! How you doing? Hope you're okay! Be careful over there! Here's Mom!"

2 **inimitable:** unique; impossible to duplicate

Mom bent over the machine and said, "Hello, Pat! Take care of your-self now! Don't do anything silly!"

Then my dad: "HEY, WHERE'S THE DOG? BRING BRUCE OVER HERE AND MAKE HIM BARK!"

Bruce barked: "Roof roof roof!"

Then, of course, my father had to point out, "THAT'S THE DOG THERE, PAT! THAT'S BRUCE THE DOG!"

We put all of about three minutes on this 90-minute tape. The next day, the same thing: "PAT, EVERYTHING IS GOOD! HERE'S THE DOG!"

"Roof roof! Roof roof!"

After a few weeks there was no more than nine minutes of tape filled, mostly the dog. Finally my father said, "Oh, let's just send the tape!" So we shipped the whole contraption off to my brother. Thinking back, I have a feeling he might have preferred a few letters.

"Quiet, Please!"

Until "The Tonight Show" became a full-time job, I spent most of every year playing one-nighters in every state of the nation. My life mystified my mother. For the longest time, she never quite understood what I did.

In 1986 I played Carnegie Hall,[3] which my parents wouldn't have missed for the world. The ushers took them to their seats, fifth row cen-ter. When I started doing my material, the crowd couldn't have been more receptive. My mother didn't know what to make of such laughter. At one point she turned around, pressed a finger to her lips and went, *Shhhhh! Quiet!*

I saw this from the stage. "Ma! Don't shush! It's a comedy show! They're *supposed* to laugh!"

This mortified her. To be singled out in public was the worst embar-rassment imaginable. And at Carnegie Hall yet!

I always told my dad if I ever made it in show business, I'd buy him a Cadillac. So as soon as I started guest-hosting for Johnny Carson, I took Dad shopping. The salesman led him directly to a new white Caddy with a red velour[4] interior. Dad wanted it on sight.

We drove it home to show my mom, who deplored ostentatiousness of any kind. She came out to meet us in the driveway and covered her eyes with shame when she saw the red velour. From that day on, when

---

3 **Carnegie Hall:** a recital hall in New York that is considered one of the most important performance spaces in the world

4 **velour:** a rich, velvety fabric

they rode around in the Cadillac, she would slump down so people wouldn't see her while my father honked at everyone in town and hollered, "HEY, MY BOY BOUGHT THIS FOR ME!"

A Lifetime Warranty.

My father loved warranties. For every product he ever bought, he would fill out the warranty card and make a copy—"for our files." Just in case.

Once when I was home for a visit, the toilet seat broke off. The hinge was rusty, and I went to throw out the seat.

My dad said, "Wait! Don't throw that away! I've got a 20-year guarantee on that thing!"

Within minutes he pulled out the warranty—a yellowed piece of paper that looked like the Magna Charta.[5]

I said, "Put that away, Dad! I am not walking down Main Street with this rotted-out toilet seat!"

"Then *I'll* do it. I've got a guarantee!"

So I drove him over to the hardware store with this awful old seat. The guy who sold it to us had retired ten years earlier. His son came out.

Dad said, "My toilet seat broke. I want a new one."

The guy looked and said, "It's rotted! I can't give you a new one."

So my dad presented him with the warranty. "Oh, yeah? Look at this! Ninety-two days left!"

The guy gave us a new seat.

The warranty on the new toilet seat promised it would last until the year 2008. When we got home, he filled out the card and made a big show of putting it in my name. This was my inheritance.

▲　▲　▲

One last story ought to give you a good idea of exactly what kind of parents they were.

When I was a teen-ager, I scraped up money to buy an old Ford pickup. Every day after school I worked on it—sanding, painting, buffing. As a present, my parents got me brand-new Naugahyde[6] upholstery for the seats.

Then once I slammed a door a little too hard, and the window shattered. I didn't have any money to replace it. I drove it anyway, including to school.

---

5 **Magna Charta:** a centuries-old English document setting out rights and privileges

6 **Naugahyde:** a vinyl-coated material

My high school was a big flat building, and you could see the parking lot from many of the classrooms. One day it began to rain. I sat in class and watched my truck—and new upholstery—get drenched through the broken window.

Suddenly I saw my mom and dad tear into the parking lot. They screeched up next to my truck and dragged a huge piece of plastic out of their car. Then, in the pouring rain, they covered up the truck.

Dad had left his office in the middle of the day, picked up Mom and bought this hunk of plastic to save my seats. I watched them do this. And I just began crying right there in class.

My parents were with me through every high and low in my life, always supportive and proud of my accomplishments. I never think of them as gone. I've got all their stories, and that keeps them nearby always. ∾

RESPONDING TO CLUSTER FOUR
Thinking Skill SYNTHESIZING

1. Each of the other clusters in this book is introduced by a question that is meant to help readers focus their thinking about the selections. What do you think the question for Cluster Four should be?

2. How do you think the selections in this cluster should be taught? Demonstrate your ideas by joining with your classmates to:

   a. create discussion questions

   b. lead discussions about the selections

   c. develop vocabulary activities

   d. prepare a cluster quiz

REFLECTING ON *WHAT'S SO FUNNY?*
Essential Question WHY DO WE NEED HUMOR?

Reflecting on this book as a whole provides an opportunity for independent learning and the application of the critical thinking skill, synthesis. *Synthesizing* means examining all the things you have learned from this book and combining them to form a greater understanding of the uses and types of humor.

There are many ways to demonstrate what you know about humor. Here are some possibilities. Your teacher may provide others.

1. After reading this book you should have a better idea of the broad range of literature that can be included in the humor category. You should also have some well-formed positions on your reading preferences regarding this genre. As you read, your position may have changed from positive to negative or vice versa or you may have decided that you liked certain humor authors and classifications but not others. Write an essay that states your opinion about reading humor. Start with an opinion statement such as "Humor must be seen or heard, rather than read, to be appreciated," or "Reading humor is (silly, fun, a waste of time, a great reliever of tension, fascinating, boring . . .). Back up your opinion with reasons that explain why you feel as you do and with examples from the selections.

2. Individually or in small groups, develop an independent project that demonstrates your knowledge of and ideas about humor. Options might include researching the lives of great comics, developing a clown act, writing satirical songs, poetry, or drama, creating a cartoon gallery, building a mini-library of humor favorites, or writing and reading aloud your own stand-up routines.

ACKNOWLEDGMENTS

Text Credits CONTINUED FROM PAGE 2 "Funny" by Nagueyalti Warren, from *Honey Hush! An Anthology of African American Women's Humor*, ed. Daryl Cumber Dance, New York: Norton, 1998. Used by permission of the author.

"Hey, You Down There" by Harold Rolseth, *Yankee Magazine*, 1971. Reprinted by permission of the Sternig & Byrne Literary Agency.

How To Eat Like A Child," copyright © 1977, 1978 by Delia Ephron, from *How To Eat Like A Child* by Delia Ephron, illustrated by Edward Koren. Used by permission of Viking Penguin, a division of Penguin Putnam, Inc.

"Humor Helps" by Carolyn J Gard, *Current Health 2®*, April/May 1998. Special permission granted, *Current Health 2®* magazine, copyright © 1998, published by Weekly Reader Corporation. All rights reserved.

Excerpt from *Leading With My Chin* by Jay Leno. Copyright © 1996 by Big Dog Productions, Inc. Reprinted by permission of HarperCollins Publishers, Inc.

"Life's A Sketch," text by Michael Neill, Bob Calandra, from *People Weekly* magazine, 4/29/96. Copyright © 1996 Time, Inc. Reprinted with permission.

"Memories of Dating" by Dave Barry. Copyright © Tribune Media Services, Inc. All rights reserved. Reprinted with permission.

From *More Letters From A Nut* by Ted L. Nancy, introduction by Jerry Seinfeld. Copyright © 1998 by Ted L. Nancy's Hand Dipped Productions. Introduction copyright © 1998 by Jerry Seinfeld. Used by permission of Bantam Books, a division of Random House, Inc.

From *More Sniglets* by Richard Hall and Friends. Copyright © 1985 by Not the Network Company, Inc. Reprinted with the permission of Simon & Schuster, Inc.

"Pancakes," copyright © 1998 by Joan Bauer. Reprinted with the permission of Simon & Schuster Books for Young Readers, an imprint of Simon & Schuster Children's Publishing Division, from *Trapped! Cages of Mind and Body* edited by Lois Duncan. Copyright © 1998 Lois Duncan.

"Shotgun Cheatham's Last Night Above Ground" by Richard Peck, from *Twelve Shots: Outstanding Short Stories About Guns* edited by Harry Mazer. Copyright © 1997 by Harry Mazer. Used by permission of Dell Publishing, a division of Random House, Inc.

From *Sinbad's Guide To Life* by Sinbad. Copyright © 1997 by David & Goliath Productions, Inc. Used by permission of Bantam Books, a division of Random House, Inc.

From *Sniglets* by Richard Hall and Friends. Copyright © 1984 by Not the Network Company, Inc. Reprinted with the permission of Simon & Schuster, Inc.

"Youngest Child Tries to Tell a Joke" by Erma Bombeck. From *Forever, Erma*, copyright © 1996 by the Estate of Erma Bombeck. Reprinted with permission of Andrews McMeel Publishing. All rights reserved.

Every reasonable effort has been made to properly acknowledge ownership of all material used. Any omissions or mistakes are not intentional and, if brought to the publisher's attention, will be corrected in future editions.

Photo and Art Credits Cover and Title Page: Joan Miró, *Portrait IV*, 1938. Oil on canvas, 130 x 97 cm. ©1999 Artists Rights Society (ARS), New York/ADAGP, Paris. Pages 4-5, 9: Gary Baseman. Page 11: TL, Corbis; TR and BL, ©FPG International; BR, Corbis/Bettmann. Page 12: TL, Lynn Goldsmith/Corbis; TR, Corbis/Bettmann; BL, Super Stock; BR, Roger Ressmeyer/Corbis. Page 15: Otmar Thorman/Photonica. Pages 16, 17, 19: Edward Koren. Page 20: Photonica. Page 29: Super Stock. Page 32: ©Brad Wilson/Photonica. Page 47: William Burlingham. Page 51: ©John Nelson/SIS. Page 52: Gary Baseman. Page 61: Robb Armstrong from *Jump Start*, courtesy United Media. Page 62: William Burlingham. Page 63-72: ©Jody Winger/SIS. Page 75: ©The New Yorker Collection 1969, George Price from cartoonbank.com. All rights reserved. Page 76: Ron Tom-Fox/The Kobal Collection. Page 83: ©The New Yorker Collection 1979, Charles Addams from cartoonbank.com. All rights reserved. Page 84: T, Mark Parisi; M, Paul Nicoloff; B, THE FAR SIDE ©1984, FARWORKS, INC. All rights reserved. Page 85: T, THE FAR SIDE ©1988, FARWORKS, INC. All rights reserved; M, John Baynham; B, THE FAR SIDE ©1985, FARWORKS, INC. All rights reserved. Page 87: Nick Kelsh. Page 94: ©Sheila Golden/SIS. Pages 100-111: Reagan Dunnick. Page 112: Howard Berman. Page 114: ©Gary Isaacs/Photonica. Page 119: ©Elliott Erwitt/Magnum Photos, Inc. Page 121: R.O. Blechman. Page 122: ©Santiago Cohen/SIS. Page 123: ©1961 Richard Taylor from *Lots of Limericks-Light, Lusty, and Lasting*, edited by Louis Untermeyer, Doubleday & Company, Inc. 1961, Garden City, NY. Pages 125, 132-133: David Merrell. Page 134, 135: Edward Koren. Page 138: Corbis/Bettmann. Page 142: © M. Gesinger/Photonica.